SOUTHERN AFR

SPIDERS

An Identification Guide

MARTIN R. FILMER

STRUIK

DEDICATION

To my son Robert, an inspiration to everyone who meets him
And to my daughter Leigh, who encouraged me to keep going for his sake.

ACKNOWLEDGEMENTS

I would like to thank the following for their many contributions: Dr Ansie Dippenaar for her inspiration, spontaneous help and advice, and for always being there; Moya Hartmann, who triggered off my interest in and love for spiders; Dr Alan Kemp, my mentor and friend in things natural; Des Louw, who provided the first conspectus which allowed me to start studying; Astri and John LeRoy, without whom there would have been no Spider Club of Southern Africa or source of practical experience in the early days; Linda Duigan, my artist, who can read my mind and 'see' the spiders in my head as I'd like to see them on paper; Vince Roth, author of *Spider Genera of North America* (American Arachnological Society, 1985), for reading the text and advising on many taxonomic changes; Annette van den Berg, Peter Croeser, Dr Gerry Newlands, Koos De Wet, Dr Joh Henschell and Andrew Smith, for their interest, advice and time spent in teaching; all those members of the Spider Club, especially Steve Langton and Lorenzo Prendini, who have collected and supplied me with specimens to work on; Tracey Groenewald for the hours spent at the photostat machine; and last but not least, my wife Sal, for her patience and encouragement throughout this project.

Struik Publishers (Pty) Ltd
(a member of the Struik Publishing Group (Pty) Ltd)
Cornelis Struik House, 80 McKenzie Street
Cape Town 8001

Reg. No.: 54/00965/07

First published 1991
Second impression 1993
Third impression 1995

Edited by Tracey Hawthorne
Designed by Petal Palmer and Odette Marais
Typeset by Bellset, Cape Town
Reproduction by Unifoto (Pty) Ltd, Cape Town
Printed and bound by Kyodo Printing Co (Pte) Ltd, Singapore

ISBN 1 86825 188 8

CONTENTS

INTRODUCTION

This book started as a much-needed attempt to fill the gap in the literature for the rank amateur, the interested naturalist-arachnologist and the budding future professional. Developing the concept, I felt myself pulled more and more to the need in southern Africa for a book of value to professionals — including, with the family information, keys to all the known genera and species. However, this required expertise and background material available only to a professional arachnologist; and how far could I go while continuously running into taxonomic changes, without losing sight of the original concept?

In an attempt to solve the problem I spent many hours discussing the project with Dr Ansie Dippenaar, curator of the National Collection of Arachnida (non-Acari) at the Plant Protection Research Institute in Pretoria. Within months of our first meetings, however, two books on South African spiders had appeared on the market, one dealing with medically important spiders and scorpions, and the other, a pocket guide in a series, limiting itself to only 23 interesting families. Although these two books catered for the rank amateur, those whose interest either required more detail or was professional were still neglected.

So we launched into the 'big one' ... but then we received a call from the Spider Club of Southern Africa for a comprehensive but not overwhelming field guide to all 63 southern African spider families, with drawings and text to allow for identification in the field and at home, using modest enlarging equipment such as a magnifying glass and torch; and including diagnostic features, special web patterns, and any specific behaviour. So we are back to an identification guide — and a book that I hope does include all the spider families that can be found and does answer most of the questions posed by amateur and professional alike.

What is a spider? Ask one hundred people this question and you'll get about a hundred different answers, ranging from 'a bug' to a 'yeech', and maybe one or two knowledgeable answers. Spiders are, perhaps, the most misunderstood creatures on earth, and this is due mainly to ignorance. The fear and dislike many people have of spiders has no real basis. From childhood man is taught to kill or avoid spiders because they are 'poisonous'. When one considers that most people come into contact with spiders — knowingly or unknowingly — in their lives without coming to any harm, it should be clear how erroneous the general concept of a spider being venomous actually is.

Spiders belong to the phylum Arthropoda, and this phylum makes up about 80 per cent of all known animals. The word 'arthropod' means 'jointed leg': arthropods have an exoskeleton (a hard outer body covering) which includes three or four pairs of legs which are jointed so that they can bend. Arthropoda have been living on earth for literally millions of years.

Arachnids, those arthropods having eight legs, have been here for about 500 million years, some 200 million years longer than the insects as we know them today. While more than a million species of insects have thus far been described, a mere 30 000 species of spiders are known. However, it is estimated that this figure represents only 30 per cent of those spiders that do actually exist and more collection and identification are required to broaden our knowledge of these fascinating creatures.

Many spiders are minute and as such are not easily seen; some, on the other hand, are veritable giants but are also not often seen because of their distribution and living habits. By far the greatest majority of those spiders encountered are the small to medium-sized, dull-coloured creatures that wander freely around the home and garden. I hope to show you the colourful spectrum of spiders that is all around us, living in a myriad habitats.

4

DIFFERENTIATION BETWEEN SPIDERS AND INSECTS

	SPIDERS	INSECTS
Body parts	Two (cephalothorax and abdomen)	Three (head, thorax and abdomen)
Legs	Eight	Six
Eyes	Normally eight, but sometimes six or even two, and always simple	Normally four, with combination of compound and simple eyes
Wings	Always absent	Most often present
Antennae	Always absent	Always present
Poison	Present in all but one family	Absent in most
Breathing	Booklungs (two, sometimes four) and often tracheae	Tracheae
Food	Always live prey	Live prey but many are herbivorous
Digestion	Takes place outside the body	Takes place inside the body
Silk	Always present and used for many purposes	Sometimes present in stages of metamorphosis and used for cocoon
Development	Spiderlings resemble adults from birth and grow by ecdysis	Young generally do not resemble adults, metamorphosing from larva to pupa to adult

HOW TO USE THIS BOOK

Using this identification guide, you should be able to identify a spider to family, and in many cases to genus. On pages 17 and 18 you will find an explanation of how the different families have been grouped; I have tried to keep, for instance, the orb-weavers together, the sheet-web spiders together and the free-living ground-dwellers together. In some cases — where, for example, the spider mimics another animal or where the male is

5

specialized, being equipped with spurs, special setae or modified palps which need to be examined under a microscope — it can be almost impossible to identify a specimen without the aid of a microscope and professional help; don't hesitate to collect the specimen and send it to the Spider Club or one of the professionals listed on page 124.

Be aware: 'shapes and sizes' is the name of the game regarding both the spiders themselves and the webs in which you may find them. So often the spider is missed in a web where it may be hiding among the debris of old prey, or it may be crouching in a retreat above the web; the web may be overlooked because it appears as a broken remnant of a full orb web. Look, examine, and be patient.

To facilitate easy reference and make this guide workable in the field, I have made use of graphic symbols for typical lifestyles, habitats, collecting methods and poison potential.

The typical lifestyles have been broken down into five basic types:

 Sedentary, web-bound (not necessarily orb web)

 Free-running, ground-living

 Sedentary, ground-living

 Free-running, plant-living

 Sedentary, plant-living

Habitats are wide and varied, so each of the graphic symbols must be viewed in the broadest possible sense. The 'built-up areas' habitat, for example, is not restricted to *only* those places mentioned, but covers any place from inner city buildings to stables on a farm. Likewise 'in and up trees' means any species of tree, not only bushveld trees or garden trees.

The habitats are as follows:

 In built-up areas

 In and up trees

 In webs between trees

 On or under bark

 In webbing, scrapes or free-running, under stones

 On or under sand

 On open ground

 On rocks or in crevices of rocks

 In burrows, web-lined or not

 On bushes and plants or in low base vegetation

 In, on or under grass

 On flowers or leaves

 In and under leaf litter and rotting logs

 In forests

 Near fresh water

 On water

On the seashore

 In semi-arid desert

 In other spiders' webs

 In disused holes

 In caves

 In association with insects

Collecting methods (see page 23) are illustrated as follows:

 Sweep-netting

 Beating

 Hand-to-jar

 Night collecting

 Pitfall trap

 Tullgren funnel

 Digging

 Sifting

 Pooter

 Rock-turning

 Tree trap

Spiders inject their poison by biting into their prey and releasing their venom through tiny holes in the tips of their fangs. Only a tiny percentage of these poisons are venomous to man. Of the 5 000 species of spiders thus far described from the region, only five or six are of medical importance and only another handful are of minor consequence.

The symbols are as follows:

 Venomous; medically important

 Mildly venomous

 Harmless; of no consequence to man

The vast majority of spiders are very small. However, a size difference of just 0,5 mm can make an enormous difference in the identification of tiny and very small spiders being studied. In order that you may immediately grasp the minuteness of some of our tiny spiders, and the large size of our tarantulas, average sizes are illustrated below, the spider being measured from the front of the carapace to the spinnerets.

Tiny: smaller than 1,5 mm

Very small: 1,5–2,5 mm

Small: 2,5–5 mm

7

Medium: 5–10 mm

Medium-large: 10–15 mm

Large: 15–30 mm

Very large: larger than 30 mm

THE ANATOMY OF A SPIDER

Arachnids, unlike insects, have only two body parts, the cephalothorax and the abdomen. All have eight legs, and antennae modified for seizing and grasping called the chelicerae. Spiders differ from other arachnids in that the abdomen is not segmented and is joined to the cephalothorax by a thin stalk, the pedicel. (The cephalothorax, which provides attachments for the four pairs of legs, the chelicerae and the pedipalps, is referred to by some writers as the prosoma while the abdomen is known as the opisthosoma.)

1. The cephalothorax

Like the abdomen, the cephalothorax is unsegmented but bears the sign of its ancestors in the form of a cervical groove demarcating the head area from the thoracic area. In many

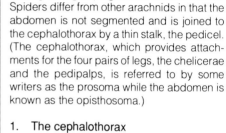

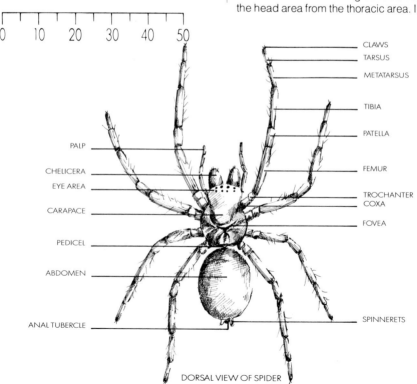

DORSAL VIEW OF SPIDER

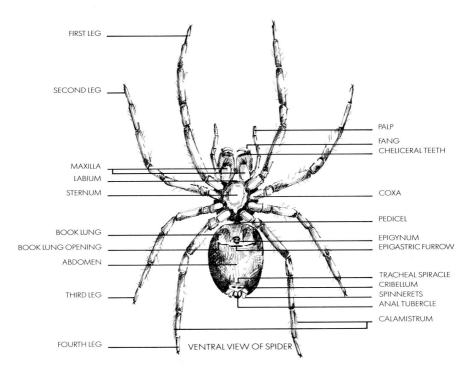

FIRST LEG

SECOND LEG

PALP
FANG
CHELICERAL TEETH

MAXILLA
LABIUM
STERNUM

COXA

PEDICEL

BOOK LUNG
BOOK LUNG OPENING
ABDOMEN

EPIGYNUM
EPIGASTRIC FURROW

TRACHEAL SPIRACLE
CRIBELLUM
SPINNERETS
ANAL TUBERCLE

THIRD LEG

CALAMISTRUM

FOURTH LEG

VENTRAL VIEW OF SPIDER

spiders this groove is difficult to detect and is mentioned here only to give location to the head area. The head area houses the eyes, the chelicerae and the mouthparts of the spider. The eyes are all simple ocelli and are usually situated at the front of the head area, often on a slightly raised protuberance. The usual number of eyes is eight but there are species with two, four or six eyes, and, some cave spiders have no eyes at all. The eyes may be set in one, two or three rows and may be of the same size or unequal in size. In a typical spider with eight eyes set in two rows of four, we can distinguish the anterior median eyes (the two middle front eyes), the anterior lateral eyes (the two outer front eyes), the posterior median eyes (the two middle back eyes) and the posterior lateral eyes (the two outer back eyes).

Often the anterior median eyes are the largest eyes (as in the family Salticidae), but irrespective of size they are always the 'main'

POSTERIOR LATERAL
POSTERIOR MEDIAN
ANTERIOR LATERAL
ANTERIOR MEDIAN

RECURVED
POSTERIOR EYE ROW

PROCURVED
ANTERIOR EYE ROW

EYE PATTERN

9

POSTERIOR MEDIAN

POSTERIOR LATERAL

ANTERIOR LATERAL

ANTERIOR MEDIAN

STRAIGHT
POSTERIOR EYE ROW

STRAIGHT
ANTERIOR EYE ROW

EYE PATTERN

eyes and differ in structure and development from the others. Because they lack a reflective layer they always appear black. The rows of eyes are frequently curved. If they are curved forward towards the front, that is, the lateral eyes are further forward than the median eyes, they are said to be procurved; and if they are curved towards the back, they are said to be recurved. When the curvature is very great and, for example in certain genera of the family Lycosidae, where the posterior median eyes are widely separated and the posterior lateral eyes are set far back on the carapace, the eyes are said to be in three rows. That area between the two rows of eyes is known as the eye space; the area between

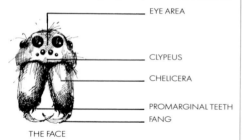

EYE AREA

CLYPEUS

CHELICERA

PROMARGINAL TEETH

FANG

THE FACE

the anterior eye row and the margin of the chelicerae is known as the clypeus; and that part of the head that can be seen when the spider is viewed directly from the front is known as the face.

The chelicerae are the first pair of appendages of the head; they are in front of and above the mouthparts. They consist of two sections: a large basal section and a smaller articulated fang which can fold down into a groove in the basal section which may or may

not have teeth-like spines on both sides. Spiders with such spines are able to crush up their prey into an unrecognizable mass. Spiders without these spines suck up their liquified prey through small bite holes. The chelicerae also allow the spider to grasp and transport prey, carry the egg sac (as in the Pisauridae) and dig burrows (as in the Ctenizidae); and, in some of the small linyphiids, the chelicerae possess stridulatory organs.

On attack the fangs are raised and held outwards following the contour of the basal section. Once the fangs have penetrated the prey the poison is injected through small apertures at the tips. In the mygalomorphs the chelicerae strike forwards and downwards (paraxial), whereas in the so-called true spiders, the araneomorphs, they work from side to side against each other (diaxial).

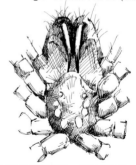

MYGALOMORPH — PARAXIAL FANGS

The mouth is a cavity situated between the pedipalps, the endites of which form the sides of the mouth. These endites are furnished with fine hairs called the scopulae, which assist in filtering out any small particles of cuticle from

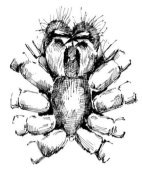

ARANEOMORPH — DIAXIAL FANGS

The ventral wall of the head, the labium, is a thickened sclerite which is movable to a lesser or greater degree (although sometimes not at all) and forms the base plate or lower lip of the mouth.

The pedipalps are the second two pairs of appendages of the head and are situated on each side of the mouth cavity. Unlike the legs, the pedipalps consist of only six segments, the metatarsus being absent. Also, there is never more than one tarsal claw on the pedipalps. In the female the pedipalps are simple structures but in the male the tarsus is highly modified for use in mating. The palp of the male is of special importance to taxonomists as each species of spider has a unique configuration. The bulb within the palp may be relatively simple in construction (in the haplogene spiders), or highly complex (in the entelegene spiders).

The thorax area of the cephalothorax is that part that bears the four pairs of jointed legs.

the crushed prey. Spiders digest their food outside their bodies by injecting into their prey, along with the killing poison, special enzymes that break up and liquify the body contents of the prey. Those spiders without the teeth-like spines on the chelicerae suck up the liquified contents, leaving a perfect shell of the victim.

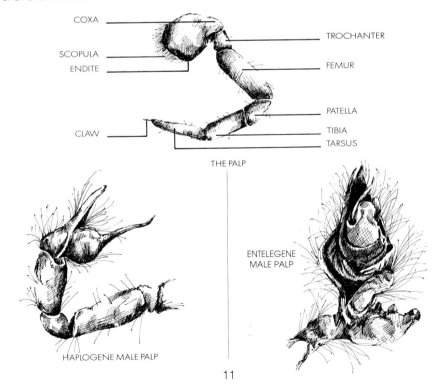

COXA

SCOPULA

ENDITE

CLAW

TROCHANTER

FEMUR

PATELLA

TIBIA

TARSUS

THE PALP

HAPLOGENE MALE PALP

ENTELEGENE MALE PALP

11

Together with the head area its dorsal aspect is termed the carapace. The plate forming the ventral wall of the thorax is called the sternum and like the carapace is hardened and stiff. It occupies the entire space between the four pairs of legs.

The legs of the spider are jointed and have their origin along the pliable connection between the carapace and the sternum. Each leg consists of seven segments: the coxa, a short, thickened base attached to the body of the spider; the trochanter, a second shortened articulation; the femur, which is long; the patella, acting as a knee joint; the tibia, which like the femur is long but is more slender; the metatarsus; and the tarsus, to which are attached two or three claws. The tarsi of many spiders are armed with fine branched hairs looking rather like a tuft, called tenet hairs. The literally thousands of end feet on these hairs allow the spider to cling to smooth surfaces by means of surface tension. The lower surface of the tarsus is also often clothed in tenet hairs; a brush of such hairs is referred to as a scopula.

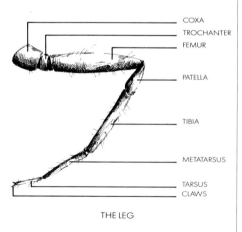

COXA
TROCHANTER
FEMUR
PATELLA
TIBIA
METATARSUS
TARSUS
CLAWS

THE LEG

All spiders have eight jointed legs, but how different these legs can be is a source of amazement: from long, extremely delicate legs to short, fat, stubby ones, and all designed for the specific spider's living habits.

Web-bound spiders, for example, are generally clumsy away from their silken homes, while the hunters would get horribly tangled up trying to traverse a web.

Apart from providing the spider with a means of locomotion, the legs are equipped with a variety of sensory organs that allow the spider to monitor its environment. Some, such as the articulated setae, function as mechanoreceptors, monitoring touch and vibration. Others, more highly refined, such as the trichobothria (very fine hairs set at right angles to the leg surface in a circular surround of cuticle), react to minute air currents and very low frequency sounds. At the leg joints are slit sensilla mechanoreceptors known as the lyriform organs, which measure the stress in the surrounding cuticle. Also at the joints are chemoreceptors in the form of open-ended hairs exposing the nerve fibres to the environment, chemosensitive hairs, and spherical pits in the dorsal surface of each tarsus known as the tarsus organs.

The eight families of spiders that spin cribellate silk have on the margin of the metatarsus of the fourth leg one or two rows of curved spines that allow them to 'comb out' the silk emanating from the cribellum and create hackle-band silk. This row of spines is known as the calamistrum.

2. The abdomen

In spiders the abdomen is unsegmented and usually soft and sac-like. It is joined to the cephalothorax by the pedicel, through which pass the blood vessels, nerves and intestine. This slender stem is often overlooked as it is usually concealed by the bulbous abdomen overhanging the carapace; however, in the more delicate spiders and those mimicking insects the pedicel is quite easily discernible.

The dorsal aspect of the abdomen often shows a set of four or more indentations which indicate the internal muscle attachment points. These points and the variations in patterns and colours on the abdomen are often of help in identifying a family. Of more importance anatomically and for the taxonomist is the ventral aspect of the abdomen.

Lying directly behind the pedicel is the epigastrium which is often more rounded than the posterior part of the abdomen. Sometimes hardened, it ends about one third the way down the abdomen in an epigastric furrow. Centred along this furrow is the opening for the reproductive organs, and at each end an opening for the booklungs. In those families having four lungs, the remaining openings occur on the more caudal portion of the abdomen. Situated along the midline but towards the spinnerets are the tracheal spiracles, which are also breathing organs.

The reproductive opening in the male is small and simple, serving only to emit the sperm which are then transmitted to the complex palps. In the mature female this outlet, known as the epigynum, opens to the two internal ovaries. The outer configuration of the epigynum, which may be very complicated, is of importance to the taxonomist in identifying the spider to species level, and may or may not be chitinized.

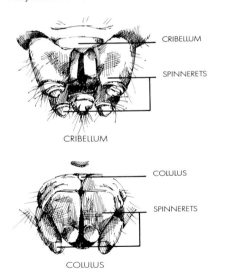

CRIBELLUM

SPINNERETS

CRIBELLUM

COLULUS

SPINNERETS

COLULUS

The spinnerets are situated at the caudal end of the abdomen, in pairs, and always on the ventral aspect. There may be two, four or six spinnerets, identified as anterior, median or posterior as they lie from the front to the back of the abdomen. In some spiders there is a specialized spinning organ known as the cribellum. (A more detailed description of the spinnerets and silk production may be found on page 19.)

The anus is situated above the posterior spinnerets.

REPRODUCTION AND GROWTH

COURTSHIP AND MATING

When it comes to reproduction, most people would say, 'I'm glad I'm not a spider!' This is not only because spiders have earned a somewhat unfair reputation for cannibalism following copulation, but also because arachnid reproduction can be highly complex both in the courtship phase and in the actual mating process.

Unique to spiders is the modification of the male palps as organs of reproduction (see page 11). As remarkable is the fact that the female epigynum is so constructed as to accept only the configuration of her conspecific male's palp. This 'lock-and-key' mechanism ensures that there can be no species mixing. (Spider taxonomists rely almost entirely on the shape and configuration of the sexual organs to determine the species of spider.)

Immature spiders are, for all practical purposes, sexless. In immature males, the palps are non-functional, as is the epigynum in immature females. These develop into functional organs of reproduction at the time of the final ecdysis into adulthood. Once fully mature, the male's single aim in life is to find a female with which to mate.

Before courting begins, the palps have to be charged with seminal fluid. In both males and females the genital pore is situated on the ventral side of the abdomen, between the booklungs; in order to transfer sperm from this pore to the palps, the male spider first spins a sperm web (a small, triangular or square web), just above the substrate. Straddling the web, he deposits a drop of sperm at its centre.

The spider then either dips his palps into the sperm or presses his palps up against the sperm from the underside of the web. The enlarged embolus of the palp draws up the fluid in much the same way an old-fashioned fountain pen would do.

Up until this time the female has lived a solitary life devoted to catching prey and feeding. Whatever moves in her vicinity she will attack and either kill or drive off; because of this, the males have evolved a complex and amazing variety of courtship rituals, only a few of which are described here. There are two main approaches, and these are based on the visual ability of the species concerned. Long-sighted spiders are mainly diurnal maters, while short-sighted ones will mate at any time.

Once a female has been located, it is up to the male to convince her that he is a male of her species and that she should succumb to his advances. In the families Lycosidae and Salticidae, which have good vision, an elaborate courtship dance is carried out by the male. The lycosid male waves his pedipalps up and down in rhythmic movements while tapping the front pair of legs on the substrate. Slowly he moves forward towards the female, awaiting a signal that she is ready to accept him and not to attack. There may be some leg-touching and rubbing before actual mating takes place. Some salticid males are adorned with elaborate hairs, often brightly coloured, on their pedipalps. Waving these, with the first pair of front legs raised high above his head, he moves in an arc around the female, waiting for her signal of acceptance. Those spiders with poor vision do not have an elaborate courtship dance, and indulge in only perhaps some leg tickling before full contact is made.

In most of the web builders, courtship is purely a tactile affair, with the male coming to the edge of the web and plucking or tapping on the silken strands to announce his presence. Some araneid males are very much smaller than their mates, and in *Argiope* the female can weigh up to a thousand times as much as the male. Obviously, the *Argiope* male has to be extra careful of not becoming a meal! In some of the larger *Araneus* species, the male approaches the female's web and tweaks the strand on which she is sitting. Invariably, he has to drop down on a drag line to avoid her initial rush forwards to attack, before clambering back up to the web and trying again ... and again and again and again! But, as the spider in the story of Robert the Bruce discovered, perseverance pays off.

Once the female has been convinced that her suitor is a prospective mate and not prey, the male spins a special mating thread on to which he must lure the female with more plucking and tweaking movements. Female araneid ardour is not long-lasting and once mating has occurred the male has to beat a fast retreat lest he be eaten. (Many spider genera do have much less complex and far more civilized mating procedures, however.)

The males of some spider families, such as the theridiids and linyphiids, are equipped with a stridulating organ. These males, once on the female's web, may stridulate, setting up a high-pitched vibration which not only brings the female out into the open, but renders her receptive to his approach.

The act of copulation can last from seconds to hours, depending on the species; in some the courtship is greatly extended and the mating very short, while in others there may be hardly any courtship with mating lasting for up to seven hours. The male inserts his palps one at a time (or, in the case of some of the more primitive spiders, both at once) into the female's epigynum and thus transfers the sperm to her.

While some spiders do live a social life of sorts, the sexes co-habiting more or less amicably in the female's web (such as species of the families Dictynidae, Eresidae and Agelenidae), there are those that eat their mates during or after copulation. This often has to do with the manner in which the male approaches the female, and the position he adopts for mating. The most notorious spouse-eating spider is *Latrodectus*, whose antisocial behaviour has earned it the common name 'black widow spider'.

There are some rather amusing methods

employed by male spiders to avoid falling prey to their prospective mates. The male of some of the pisaurid species will catch a fly and neatly enswathe it in silk then, holding the wrapped gift in his chelicerae, he approaches the female. Once she has accepted it and has started eating it, he nips around and proceeds to mate. The males of some of the crab spiders are tiny in comparison to their mates. To overcome his size disadvantage, such an undersized male will set about casting strands of silk to and fro across the female's abdomen while she is lying in wait for prey, virtually tying her down like the Lilliputians tied down Gulliver. Once she is thus secured, he mates with her and then leaves her to her own devices. She may take several hours to extricate herself.

Once inseminated, the female may hold the sperm in her spermathaecae for days or even months, using only the amount needed to fertilize the eggs she lays at any one time. She is thus able to lay a number of egg sacs full of fertile eggs after only one mating. Araneomorph spiders, equipped with the inner organs within the abdominal wall, can ecdyse and retain viable sperm for the next egg-laying; mygalomorph spiders, however, are evaginated during ecdysis and so are rendered virginal at each moult, making it necessary for them to mate again in order to lay fertile eggs. Gestation periods differ enormously between species and are related to the spider's lifespan.

Generally, the smaller the spider the fewer eggs are laid in each egg sac, but many of the smaller species make more than one egg sac at a time or over a period of time. Larger spiders tend to make one large egg sac containing large numbers of eggs. The number of shapes and sizes of egg sacs is legion, and many methods of camouflage are used to hide them.

Some spiders, such as the heteropodids and the oxyopids, stay with the egg sac and guard it until the young hatch; some, like the Pisauridae, provide a nursery in which the spiderlings may live in safety until they have reached their second or third instar and are able to fend for themselves; and others, such as the Lycosidae, carry the young around on their backs until they are ready to disperse.

GROWTH AND DISPERSAL

Spiders emerge from their eggs as carbon copies of their parents and grow rapidly by a series of skin sheddings, called ecdysing, developing from one instar to the next until finally reaching the sexually mature stage.

When the old skin has been shed there is rapid growth until the new, pliable skin hardens and effectively halts any further growth. The occupant is then obliged to wait for the next ecdysis before getting any bigger! The smaller the spider, the fewer the moults required to attain adulthood. Medium-sized spiders ecdyse approximately seven times, and the larger varieties up to 10 times. Generally, spiders seek a quiet place to ecdyse for they are at their most vulnerable during and immediately after moulting.

When still very young some spiderlings disperse by means of ballooning; that is, they climb up to the highest vantage point they can find (a small tree, maybe a fence post) and then, facing into the wind, they raise their bodies as high as they can and emit strands

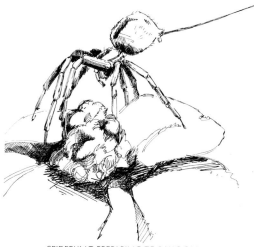

SPIDERLING PREPARING TO BALLOON

of silken threads from the spinnerets. Soon there is enough silk to be carried on the wind, and the spiderling floats away from its birth place to find a new home. Many thousands of tiny spiders lose their lives, but sufficient numbers survive to start up colonies elsewhere and spread the species. It is quite common to have spiderlings landing on the decks of ships thousands of miles from land. In experiments carried out by naturalist/filmmaker David Attenborough, ballooning spiders were collected miles above the earth's surface in the upper layers of the stratosphere, none the worse for wear!

By our standards most spiders live very short lives, growing from spiderlings to adults, then dying, all within one year. There are spiders, especially the mygalomorphs, that are known to live for up to 20 years but the great majority of the species live for less than 18 months. Male spiders always live shorter lives than females.

LIFESTYLES AND HABITATS

Eight eyes means four times better vision, right? No, not at all. What the spider sees we cannot really imagine, for while we observe our environment primarily with our eyes, the great majority of spiders are to all intents and purposes almost blind, and use their other senses to keep in touch with the world around them. The wandering hunters do have better vision than do their web-bound counterparts, but even they do not rely entirely on their

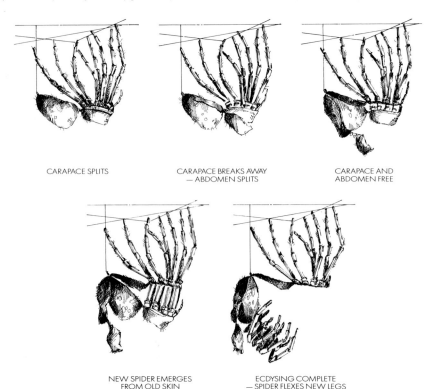

CARAPACE SPLITS

CARAPACE BREAKS AWAY
— ABDOMEN SPLITS

CARAPACE AND
ABDOMEN FREE

NEW SPIDER EMERGES
FROM OLD SKIN

ECDYSING COMPLETE
— SPIDER FLEXES NEW LEGS

ECDYSING SPIDER

vision. The family Salticidae has perhaps the most sophisticated visual apparatus, with the main anterior median eyes allowing a degree of binocular vision so that the spider may estimate distance — they are able to focus reasonably for up to three or four centimetres.

The key to spiders' senses lies in the sense organs situated on their legs. These take the form of various types of sensory hairs and slits in the outer integument of the legs, which allow the spider to 'sense' the environment around it with great accuracy (see page 12).

Spiders live everywhere, from the top of the dome of St Paul's Cathedral in London to the stopes of Johannesburg's gold mines; from the blistering heat of the Namib Desert to the frozen northern coasts of Greenland. Although there are exceptions to every rule, spiders may be generally classified according to their various lifestyles.

1. THE WEB-BOUND SPIDERS

To most people a spider is synonymous with a web, and a web, in turn, with an orb web. More than half of all known spiders spin some form of web for prey capture, but only a few of these spin an orb web.

The orb-web spiders. These spiders build their unique structural masterpieces in open spaces between trees, branches of trees or man-made objects such as fence wires. The webs may vary in size from a few centimetres to a few metres across. The spider sets up home either in the web, usually at the hub, or up and away in a retreat which is connected to the hub by means of a signal line. Most orb webs are vertical or built at a slight angle, but some are horizontal, especially those of the family Uloboridae. Some of the families classified as orb builders are Araneidae, Nephilidae, Tetragnathidae and Uloboridae. However, some genera within these families do not spin orb webs, for example, *Cladomelea* of the family Araneidae, which spins a sticky ball on a silken thread which it whirls around like a bolus to catch prey.

The tunnel-web, tubular-web and tangled-web spiders. Spiders living in tubes or tunnels in the ground, under stones and rocks, in holes and cracks of trees and in human artifacts such as poles, tins and cracked walls generally line the sides of their abode with a silken sheet, rounding off the entrance with a ridge of silk and debris or closing it with a tight-fitting trapdoor. Often radiating from the entrance is a spiral of trap lines to inform the spider of approaching prey. The members of one family of mygalomorph spiders, the Atypidae, live in an enclosed silken tube for their entire life. Part of this tube is constructed under the ground, with the section above the ground lying horizontally. Prey moving over this section is affixed by a pair of extremely long and sharp fangs thrust through the wall by the spider lurking within the tube. Families using tunnel webs are most of the mygalomorph spiders discussed in the second part of the book and, among the so-called true spiders, the Amaurobiidae, Filistatidae and Segestriidae, and some genera of the Eresidae, Lycosidae and Oecobiidae.

The sheet-web spiders. This web, as its name implies, looks much like a silken sheet and is usually built close to the substrate. The web may vary in size from some 12 centimetres to tiny sheets of less than one centimetre across. These sheet webs house such families as the Agelenidae, Cyatholipidae, Hahniidae, Oecobiidae and Linyphiidae, and some members of the family Lycosidae.

The scaffold-web and lace-web spiders. These spiders build three-dimensional webs which allow them to capture prey coming from above or below the central section housing the retreat. The family most often associated with this kind of web is the Theridiidae, but the nesticids also build scaffold webs. Also placed in this group are the tiny dictynid spiders and the pholcids.

The net-throwing spiders. One family of spiders, the Deinopidae, uses a retiarius or gladiator-net to throw over passing prey.

The kleptoparasites. These are spiders that live in the webs of other spiders, either preying on the host spider or feeding on prey remains in the web. The Mimetidae and the tiny silver dew-drop spiders of the family Theridiidae fall into this group.

17

2. GROUND-LIVING SPIDERS

The burrow-living spiders. Although there are a few araneomorphs which are regarded as 'burrow-living', they are not confined to these burrows, so I have decided to place all the mygalomorphs under the burrow-living spiders. Those genera of the families Lycosidae and Zodariidae which are araneomorphs and do dig burrows are not necessarily confined to them, so are included under the free-living spiders.

The free-living spiders. Smaller than the more sedentary burrow dwellers and both diurnal and nocturnal, these spiders may be seen running freely over all sorts of substrates. Those spiders living near or on water are genera of the families Pisauridae and Lycosidae. Intertidal spiders belong to the families Desidae, Anyphaenidae, Erigoninae and Hahniidae. Spiders living on, in and around rocks may come from the families Oecobiidae, Hersiliidae, Selenopidae, Ctenidae and Eresidae. Desert spiders come from the families Sicariidae and Eresidae. Spiders found in the disturbed soil in and around termite mounds are members of the family Ammoxenidae. Finally, those living with man in his abode come mainly from the families Clubionidae, Heteropodidae, Agelenidae, Gnaphosidae, Pholcidae, Salticidae and Theridiidae.

3. THE PLANT-LIVING SPIDERS

Different spiders live on different plants and each spider family is uniquely adapted to its chosen way of life. Some are agile and leap from leaf to leaf in pursuit of their prey, such as members of the family Oxyopidae, while others spend their entire life on a single part of the plant, as do genera belonging to family Thomisidae.

The grass dwellers. Many spiders live on the stems and blades of grass. They tend to take on the colour of the grass in which they live and are mostly yellowish-brown to dull green. Ambushers, they await their prey clinging to the stems, front legs stretched out in front of them. Genera of the families Thomisidae and Philodromidae live in the grass.

The flower dwellers. Who hasn't seen one of the brightly coloured, fat, female crab spiders of the family Thomisidae, matching the colour of the flower on which she is sitting? In pinks, yellows, pale greens and white, they wait in ambush for insects visiting the flower for nectar.

The foliage dwellers. Like the grass dwellers, these spiders vary in colour from fawn to bright green. Free-running and living their whole lives on one plant, they may move around rapidly or lie in wait and only now and then dash out to attack passing prey. Foliage dwellers include members of the families Oxyopidae, Clubionidae and Heteropodidae.

The bark dwellers. These spiders tend to be flattened either minimally or, as in the family Trochanteriidae, grossly. They vary in colour from grey to dark brown and black. Remaining motionless unless provoked, they can move with incredible speed. Bark dwellers of the families Hersiliidae and Trochanteriidae live entirely on, in or under the bark of trees, both dead and alive. Some bark dwellers, on the other hand, use the bark of trees as a retreat when not hunting, as do genera of the family Araneidae, or camouflage themselves by pulling up the legs against the abdomen, to resemble a dried-out bud or thorny growth on the tree, as does *Caerostris*.

The habitat of spiders is almost universal and as you go through this book you will discover many more places where spiders have made their homes. However, using the above broad categories, I have arranged the families according to where you are most likely to find them. Clearly there are exceptions to every rule (eg. genera of the orb-web weavers such as *Aethriscus*, the bird-dropping spider, and *Cladomelea*, the bolus spider, do not make webs, let alone an orb web !) But on the whole every effort has been made to flow from one 'habitat and lifestyle' to the next while retaining some sort of continuity. Within each group the spider families are listed alphabetically and not according to size, and possible variations within any one family will become evident as you read through the text.

THE SILK OF SPIDERS

All spiders possess silk glands and spinnerets to produce silk threads. Unlike those insects that are able to produce silk only to build cocoons for pupating, most spiders from the first instar can spin silken threads for a variety of functions. A protein, silk is produced inside the body of the spider by up to six distinct glands. Each gland produces a very specific type of silk, designed for a special function, but only a few families have all six glands. Most spiders have at least three or four of the six glands.

Tubuliform glands are found only in the female spider, as it is she who produces the cocoon. All males, on the other hand, possess anciniform glands for the production of their sperm web. Spiders not using silk for prey capture lack aggregate glands, while these are most typical of the orb-web spiders.

One assumes that the thread being released from the spider's body is one solid line, but under a microscope it can be seen that it is made up of numerous fine strands. (The breaking strain of spider silk is greater weight for diameter than steel!) Each gland leads to a spinneret, which is made up of thousands of tiny spigots. Silk is emitted from the spigots not by muscular pressure but by the pressure of the silk emanating from the glands. The spider may drop down while producing its silken thread, or walk away from a point of attachment while feeding out its silk, or pull out the silk with its fourth legs, or allow the wind to extract the silk as the spider is about to balloon. The silk does not dry as it comes into contact with the air; rather, it is an aligning of the tiny molecules in the silk that renders each thread stable and 'dry' as it leaves the spider's body.

The cribellate spiders possess an additional spinning organ, the cribellum, which is situated in front of the anterior spinnerets. This oblong, sieve-like plate may be a single organ or be divided by a keel or keels to be a bipartite, tripartite or quadripartite organ. It is fed by many thousands of spigots, and the very fine threads emanating are combed out into a hackled band by the rhythmic movements of the calamistrum on the fourth leg of the spider, rather like a woman teasing her hair with a teasing comb. Hackle-band silk feels sticky to the touch although it contains no viscid silk like that produced by the aggregate glands.

Spiders form two major groups, the wandering or hunting spiders and the web-bound spiders. The wanderers make use of attachment discs, drag lines and silks for reproduction, but species of the web-bound spiders may make use of all six glands, for example

GLAND	FUNCTION	SPINNERETS USED
Ampullate glands	For drag lines For frame threads	Anterior Median
Piriform glands	For attachment discs	Anterior
Aciniform glands and tubuliform glands	For enswathing silk, sperm web and the outer wall of the egg sac	Median and posterior
Aggregate glands	For glue of sticky spiral	Posterior
Flagelliform glands	Axial thread of sticky spiral	Posterior

Araneus, with its well-known orb or wagon-wheel web, spins every kind of silk to meet the needs of its everyday life.

Some web spiders (spiders using their webs, of whatever construction, to catch prey) use their silk for lining their abode, most often a tunnel or burrow, or down a crack or crevice. While the silk itself is not used for catching prey, in many cases it is used to construct trip lines, radiating out from the entrance of the burrow to relay to the spider, waiting at the entrance, the movements of approaching prey.

Sheet webs, as made by the families Agelenidae and Linyphiidae, are easily recognized, especially in the early morning when the dew has settled on them. They provide the spider with a retreat or living area, catch threads to knock down prey and an open sheet-like plain over which the spider can run to catch the prey.

Like sheet webs, scaffold webs (so-called because they resemble a scaffold) have catch threads. Here, however, there are catch threads above and below the main frame, lying with and attached to the mooring threads that hold the whole web together. The threads above the frame serve as knockdown lines, while those attached to the substrate most often are studded with sticky silken droplets to ensnare passing crawling or jumping insects.

Specialized webs, such as the retiarius web of the family Deinopidae and the bolas of the family Araneidae (genus *Cladomelea*), are discussed in full under those families.

Orb webs are without doubt everyman's concept of a spider's web. Whatever the spider, wherever the habitat, most people if asked to draw 'the spider's home' would draw an orb web. The construction of the web, which is often a daily occurrence in which the spider puts up the web at dusk only to dismantle it at dawn, follows certain steps.

1. The bridge. The spider either sits at a point near to where the web is to be built and spins a number of silken threads, allowing the wind to direct their path to another attachment point, whereupon she crosses backwards and forwards, laying down additional threads to reinforce the bridge line; or she starts at a point and walks across the substrate, letting out a drag line to be pulled up to form a bridge line, until she finds a suitable attachment point. Often the bridge line may span a considerable distance. (We illustrate only the first method here.)

2. The foundation lines. Once the bridge has been reinforced by continual crossings and the laying down of additional threads, the spider moves to a second point, lower down, throwing out a drag line behind her, and attaches this to a suitable point by means of an attachment disc. She repeats this step at various points, moving downwards, across and back up to the opposite side of the bridge line. Thus she constructs the 'frame' or foundation lines within which the orb will be made.

3. The radii. Yet another line is stretched across the bridge line, and the spider takes up a position at the middle of this thread. She draws it downwards, to where the centre of the web will be, then continues downwards on one strand to the first available attachment point, where she secures the thread with an attachment disc. Within the framework is now a 'Y' of silken thread. These three threads make up the first radii, and around these the spider continues to make further radii at regular intervals.

4. The hub. The hub is the centre of the web, where the radii converge. It may be strengthened by a mesh of silken threads, reinforced by a network of criss-cross patterns or left open. Some species extend the hub in the form of a stabilimentum — radiating outwards horizontally or vertically — or in the form of a cross.

5. The dry-silk zone. Moving outwards from the hub, the spider constructs a varying number of spirals with 'dry' (not sticky) silk. She attaches the radii at right angles, drawing them together in even lengths for perhaps six to 12 circles.

6. The catch-web or viscid zone. Starting from an external point on the frame, the spider spins a viscid thread, moving around and inwards in closely arranged spirals until the outer edge of the free zone (that area where no spirals will be constructed) is reached. Some species take up a position in the middle of the hub, hanging upside-down, waiting for prey to fly into the web; some wait on the periphery; and others build a trap line.

7. **The trap line.** Trap line builders build a retreat above and to the side of the web. This retreat is connected to the hub by a sturdy thread, allowing the spider to move freely between the open web and the hidden retreat. It also serves as the communication between the spider and the struggling, ensnared prey.

The stabilimentum Various theories have been put forward as to the real function of the stabilimenta made by some species of orb-web spiders. The most accepted of these are that this structure serves as a strengthening mechanism, a warning to large flying insects or birds that may destroy the web if they hit it and a place to weave in debris and prey remains among which the spider can conceal itself. The main family of orb weavers is the Araneidae, but other families that build orb webs include the Tetragnathidae, Metidae and Nephilidae, and some of the genera within the cribellate spider family Uloboridae.

A NOTE ON POISONS

All spiders bar the Uloboridae possess poison glands, but all spiders are not poisonous. A few species may be referred to as potentially venomous to man, that is, their poison has either a cytotoxic or a neurotoxic effect if injected into human tissue, but one would have to eat a spider and suffer the symptoms of poisoning from its body contents to be 'poisoned' by it. Apart from the fact that most

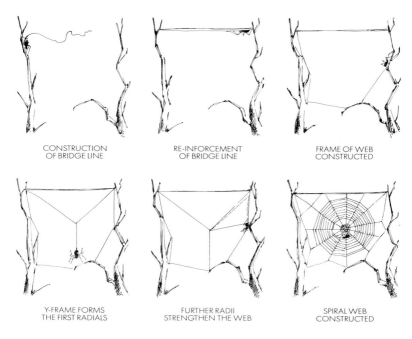

CONSTRUCTION
OF BRIDGE LINE

RE-INFORCEMENT
OF BRIDGE LINE

FRAME OF WEB
CONSTRUCTED

Y-FRAME FORMS
THE FIRST RADIALS

FURTHER RADII
STRENGTHEN THE WEB

SPIRAL WEB
CONSTRUCTED

CONSTRUCTION OF ORB WEB

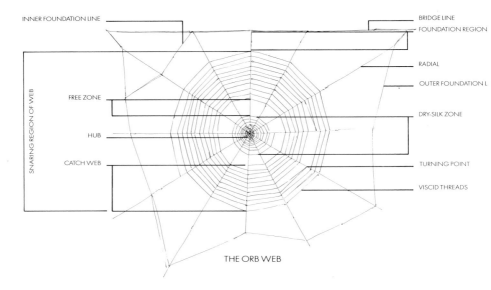

THE ORB WEB

spiders are so small that their chelicerae are not robust enough to pierce human skin, those species that can are most often loath to do so. They would all rather run and hide than confront so large an aggressor.

A pair of poison glands is situated in the cephalothorax, each gland consisting of a sac-like section in which the poison is stored and a long, tapering duct section which terminates at the tip of the fang as a tiny opening. Surrounding the gland are striated muscles which contract, ejecting the venom through the tapering duct.

As is the case with snake bite, there are a number of factors that influence the severity of a spider bite: 1. the amount of venom the spider is able to inject; 2. the site of the bite (a bite on the face would obviously have more effect than one on the foot); and 3. the age and health of the victim, as well as any personal allergies.

Spiders potentially venomous to man have typically two types of poison: neurotoxic and cytotoxic. Neurotoxic poison affects the neuromuscular synapses and causes heart palpitations, dyspnoea (difficult breathing), raised blood pressure, severe pains in the chest and abdomen, and a condition of extreme fear and anxiety. Only one family, Theridiidae (genus *Latrodectus*), is of medical importance, and only the black button spider, *Latrodectus indistinctus*, warrants immediate medical attention. The bite of neurotoxic spiders is painful.

Cytotoxic poison affects the cellular tissue around the site of the bite, and in some instances tissue throughout the body. The bite is painless and the first symptom may be just a raised red bump, rather like that caused by a mosquito bite. Severe symptoms develop slowly, the bump becoming painful, then ulcerating into a large surface lesion which may cover up to 10 centimetres in diameter. These types of lesions are encountered when the spider involved is from the families Loxoscelidae (genus *Loxosceles*) or Clubionidae (genus *Cheiracanthium*). Lesions of even greater severity and tissue damage at all levels throughout the body is most likely to have been caused by a spider of the family Sicariidae (genus *Sicarius*). Not well documented in man but proved in animal tests, the poison of *Sicarius* is the most virulent cytotoxin we know of in the region.

COLLECTING SPIDERS

Conservative estimates put arachnological fauna at some 250 000 spiders per arable acre of land in the world. By collecting spiders live or preserving them in alcohol you will not be denuding the population. Rather, you will be adding to current knowledge, expanding the collections and helping our professionals. Specimens should be labelled with the following information:

LOCALITY: When noting where the specimen was collected, include map references if possible and always write down the name of the province.

DATE: Make a note of when it was caught.

HABITAT: Include a short description of the specimen's immediate surroundings, for example, if it was taken from a web or from under a stone or found on the bark of a tree.

NAME: Write down your name as collector.

FAMILY: Make a tentative identification if possible.

It is true that some of the larger genera of spiders can be diagnosed in the field; indeed the large *Nephila* species can be identified to species level with the naked eye. However, the great majority of the spiders you collect will need to be studied under a magnifying glass or microscope from the top, the bottom and often other angles. This is impossible with the spider running to and fro in the bottle; a dead, wet specimen may be viewed at leisure, time and time again.

The quickest and easiest way of collecting is by means of a **sweeping net**. Sweeping nets are used by professional arachnologists to sample specified sections of grasslands within certain defined areas; the same demarcated area is swept again and again at different times of the year to monitor spider populations. A sweeping net may be made from a landing net commonly used by fisher-

men. Remove the fish netting and replace it with some sturdy white material such as thick linen, which should be at least twice as deep as the frame of the net is wide. Do not use coloured or patterned materials as these render small spiders almost impossible to see. If

SWEEPING NET

possible buy a fish net that has a solid round metal frame and a removable, screw-in aluminium handle. This will give you two nets in one: a sweeping net and a **beating net.**

As a collector you will be using your net to sweep through tall grass and weeds to pick up small to medium-sized spiders of many varieties. Unscrew the handle, hold the net section under the branch of a tree or a clump of small branches of a bush, and beat the foliage with the handle to knock down spiders living among the leaves and branches. The sweeping net can also be used to collect ground dwellers. Simply gather up a wad of leaf litter and spread it out onto the sweeping net, and sift through it. Many small spiders are found in this way. Real enthusiasts will even use a sieve to get rid of the larger leaves first and then sift through the debris.

Some collectors prefer to use a beating tray. As with the sweeping net, spiders fall into the beating net or tray and are then transferred to the kill-bottle, or to aerated bottles if you want to keep the specimens alive.

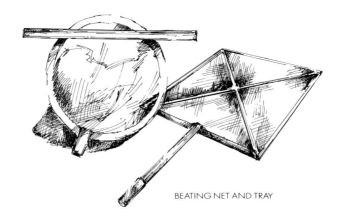

BEATING NET AND TRAY

Many families of spiders may be collected by the simple **hand-to-jar** method. Place a wide-mouthed bottle next to the spider and coax the spider into it using a probe of some kind. I use a camel-hair paint brush, but a twig from the nearest tree would work as well. Although there are only a few medically dangerous spiders, all spiders can bite; 'hand-to-jar' does not mean physically picking up the specimen and putting it into a bottle, especially when dealing with one of the more venomous species! Orb-web spiders are most easily found by walking towards the sun either early in the morning or just before sundown. In the morning you will have the added advantage of glistening dew highlighting the silken threads. In the morning, too, you will be able to spot the sheet webs of the agelenid and linyphiid spiders more easily. Under fallen trees and rocks, and often under debris such as building material, you can find a myriad spider species which can be collected hand-to-jar.

In among leaf litter on the forest floor live some minute spiders, best collected by means of a **tullgren funnel**. A wad of leaves is placed in a wide-mouthed funnel, the base of which has been covered with a coarse sieve. The tube of the funnel is placed in a container such as a old tin into which some alcohol has been poured. The tiny spiders make their way through the litter and down the tube, and fall into the alcohol. (A bright lamp positioned over the funnel will drive some spiders down more quickly as the leaf litter-dwellers always avoid bright light.) As an alternative, you could leave out the alcohol and collect the spiders live. If you opt to do this, remember to check the funnel regularly, otherwise you will be left with only one spider in the trap — the biggest, which will have eaten all the others!

TULLGREN FUNNEL

Another technique for catching ground dwellers is the ground trap or **pitfall trap**. A medium-sized plastic potting container is set into the ground so that the top is flush with ground level. A funnel made of an old X-ray plate (or some other stiff, slippery material such as smooth cardboard or thick plastic) is

PIT FALL TRAP

placed in the pot and the trap is covered with a large flat stone or piece of tin, propped up with small stones, to keep out predators and the rain. Any unsuspecting spider walking

into the funnel will slide down and into the container. The trap may be left dry and live specimens collected regularly; or alcohol may be placed in a container within the pot to kill and preserve specimens, and the trap left unattended and cleaned out once a week.

A **pooter** or camel-hair brush may be used to suck or dislodge small spiders from rock faces or household walls. A pooter can be made by using rubber tubing, a collecting bottle, a small piece of gauze and some glue or silicone sealant. The spider is covered with the wider, longer tube while you give a short, sharp suck on the shorter tube. The spider is drawn into the collecting bottle, but prevented from being sucked into the mouth by the gauze affixed to the sucking tube.

Tunnel-dwellers may be extricated by **digging** but this is best left to those collectors who know how to do it without endangering the occupant at the bottom of the tunnel. Join your local spider club or society and go along on the outings with experienced collectors.

Many spiders are collected more easily at **night**. A headlamp torch is the one to use. The lamp section is worn on the forehead and tilted downwards enough to throw the beam about six metres ahead of you. The eyes of

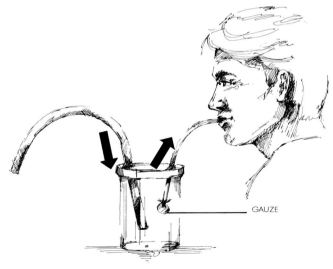

GAUZE

POOTER

25

NIGHT COLLECTING WITH THE AID OF A HEAD LAMP

lycosids, heteropodids and pisaurids reflect in the light, and the spider may be approached and trapped in a collecting bottle.

Finally, there is the **tree trap**, which is nothing more or less than a strip of corrugated cardboard wrapped around the trunk of a tree and secured there with sturdy string or wire. Spiders living on the tree will use the cavities made by the corrugations as retreats, and if the trap is left for two to three weeks, quite a number of interesting spiders may be caught.

A live specimen can be kept in a reasonably small bottle, providing the lid is perforated. If it is not possible to transfer the spider to a larger container within a few days, a small wad of damp cottonwool should be placed in the bottle as live spiders require a constant supply of water. In large cages it is best to have the water in a shallow dish. If the spider is very small a length of wool can be inserted through one of the holes in the lid and wetted from the outside. Water will then become available to the spider inside without any possibility of waterlogging it.

Preserving spiders is best done in 70 per cent alcohol to which has been added about half a teaspoon of glycerine per litre. The spider may be put directly into the alcohol where, apart from losing some of its colour, it will be preserved indefinitely. The glycerine renders the specimen soft and pliable for future microscopic examination. Large spider specimens left for 10 to 12 weeks in alcohol in a refrigerator can be set out with entomological pins on polystyrene. The alcohol will preserve the spider and the refrigeration will prevent certain of the enzymes in the abdomen from destroying the soft tissues and thus prevent the abdomen from shrivelling as the spider dries out. To display the specimen, apply a small quantity of cold glue to its feet, and encase it in a see-through container.

ARANEOMORPHS

Araneomorphs are tiny to very large spiders that belong to the suborder Labidognatha. They are characterized by having only one pair of booklungs and diaxial chelicerae that work from side to side against each other. The majority of the web-making spiders are araneomorphs.

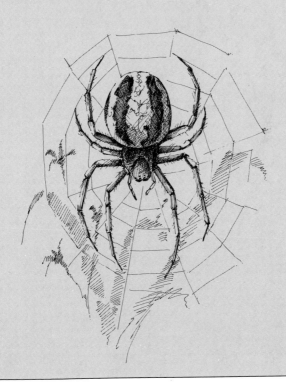

Orb-Web Spiders

FAMILY: **Araneidae**

ORB-WEB SPIDERS

POISON: Family as a whole is harmless
COLLECTING METHODS: Sweep-netting;
beating; hand-to-jar; night collecting; pooter; tree trap

The araneids are a large family and are very diverse in shape, colouring and behaviour. The sexes differ greatly in size and shape, the mass of the female sometimes being as much as a thousand times that of the male.

Araneids always have three claws, and the third leg is always the shortest.

The orb weavers spin webs as traps in which to ensnare prey, and these are both structurally perfect for their function and things of great beauty.

The family is divided into different subfamilies of which three are known to occur in southern Africa.

SUBFAMILY: **Argiopinae**

GARDEN ORB-WEB SPIDERS

COMMON GENERA: *Argiope, Gea*

 ·

LIFESTYLE: Sedentary, web-bound
HABITAT: In built-up areas; in and up trees; in webs between trees; on bushes and plants or in low base vegetation; in, on or under grass
SIZE: Very large. >30 mm up to approximately 70 mm. Female much larger than male
DIURNAL

Most of the *Argiope* species are large, conspicuous spiders, recognized by the silvergrey carapace, lobed and banded, most often yellow, black and silver abdomen, and banded, long legs. *Gea* is smaller than most argiopes and has an arched carapace. The abdomen has a distinctive colour pattern.

Argiope spiders (see plate 1) spin large webs, usually in tall grass or low bushes, often in suburban gardens. The web has a characteristic zigzag stabilimentum. Once spun it remains in position and the spider will make running repairs to it if it is damaged.

The female hangs upside-down in the centre of the web with the front two pairs of legs held together and forwards and the back two pairs held together and backwards, forming a cross. In those species where the stabilimentum itself takes the form of a cross, the legs of the spider rest up against it.

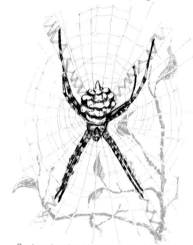

Garden orb-web spider, in web with stabilimentum

All the argiopes react in the same way to prey ensnared in the web. They approach it, turn, and with a rapid action of the two pairs of back legs draw out sheets of silken threads from the spinnerets and enswathe the prey. Only then do they bite through the wrapping, kill the victim and proceed to feed. This technique of prey capture is not unique to this subfamily but is common among most of the araneids. If not particularly hungry at the time of prey capture the spider will carry the prey to the edge of the web and hang it there for future consumption.

The female garden orb-web spider spins an egg sac that is characteristically camouflaged according to her environment.

SUBFAMILY: Gasteracanthinae
KITE SPIDERS

COMMON GENERA: Gasteracantha, Isoxya, Afracantha

LIFESTYLE: Sedentary, web-bound
HABITAT: In and up trees; in webs between trees; on bushes and plants or in low base vegetation; in forests
SIZE: Medium to medium-large. 5–15 mm. Female much larger than male
DIURNAL

Kite spider at the centre of her web

The abdomen is shiny, hard and dorsally flattened and has a number of spiny projections laterally and posteriorly. The bright red, orange, yellow, white and black on the abdomen render this spider unmistakable. The male is darker in colour than the female.

In *Gasteracantha* (see plate 2) the abdomen is much wider than it is long, and usually has long spurs to the side. *Isoxya* has a squarish abdominal plate with projections at the four corners and on the posterior.

The spinnerets are centred on the ventral aspect of the abdomen and are raised on a projection which is surrounded by a ring of hardened integument.

It is the female and juvenile kite spiders that are seen hanging in the centre of orb webs spun vertically or inclined at an angle of 45 degrees. The web is often made between two low *Acacia* trees or in forests, about 2 m above the ground. Sometimes it may be found high up between the tops of trees.

Kite spiders take up a position in the centre of the web and wait for prey to fly into the snare threads. The method of prey capture is typical of the other orb weavers (see page 28).

SUBFAMILY: Araneinae
TYPICAL ORB WEAVERS

COMMON GENERA: Araneus, Neoscona, Cyclosa, Cyrtophora, Caerostris, Nemoscolus, Pycnacantha, Paraplectana, Cladomelea, Aethriscus, Singa, Larinia

This subfamily includes genera having such distinctive characteristics of looks and behaviour that each genus is treated separately.

A. *ARANEUS AND NEOSCONA* (HAIRY FIELD SPIDERS)

LIFESTYLE: Sedentary, web-bound
HABITAT: In built-up areas; in and up trees; in webs between trees; on bushes and plants or in low base vegetation; in, on or under grass; in forests
SIZE: Medium to medium-large. 4–16 mm. Female larger than male
NOCTURNAL

Araneus and *Neoscona* (see plates 3 and 5) are the best known of all the medium to medium-large orb weavers. They resemble each other in having the abdomen usually wider

29

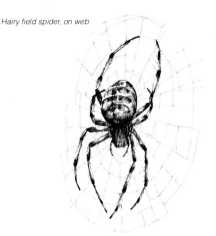

Hairy field spider, on web

than it is long, raised near the anterior, oval or triangularly oval in outline, and often overhanging the carapace. Colour varies from cream to brown to black, usually with distinct patterns dorsally.

The eyes are set in two rows, with the lateral eyes almost contiguous. The legs are shorter than those of the argiopids and when at rest they fold over or under the body.

The two genera differ in the shape of the thoracic groove, which is usually longitudinal in *Neoscona* and transverse in *Araneus*.

The males of both genera are smaller and much more angular than the females, and have a less hairy carapace and abdomen. The legs of the males are usually well armed with strong spines, and the pedipalps in mature specimens challenge those of the males of the family Theridiidae (see page 69) in size.

The orb webs of the hairy field spiders vary from tiny and frail to large and robust but always epitomize the 'perfect orb'. They are spun between two prominent points and are often attached to man-made structures. Most species build the orb web in the late evening and dismantle it at daybreak.

During the hours of darkness the spider takes up a position hanging upside-down at the hub of the web, and during the day either moves up and into a retreat above the web site after removing the web or hides under the bark of one of the trees to which the web was

attached, sometimes in a retreat.

A characteristic behaviour pattern of hairy field spiders is their tendency to drop from the hub of the web on a single thread if disturbed, and then either hang suspended there or drop to the substrate: *Araneus* must surely be the spider that dropped down beside Little Miss Muffet!

B. *CYCLOSA* (GARBAGE LINE SPIDER)

 ·

LIFESTYLE: Sedentary, web-bound
HABITAT: In webs between trees; on bushes and plants or in low base vegetation; in, on or under grass; in forests
SIZE: Medium to medium-large. 5–15 mm
DIURNAL

Garbage line spider, on web

In female *Cyclosa* the abdomen has a distinct caudal tubercle protruding past the spinnerets, which varies in size and becomes more prominent with age. It is absent in males. The abdomen is usually silver or grey. The first pair of legs is longer than the rest.

The eyes are situated on a prominent tubercle at the front of a usually shiny brownish carapace.

The garbage line spider builds its web between grasses and bushes. The web may be distinguished from those of other orb weavers by its having a stretched stabilimentum

30

across the centre of a meshed hub (distinct from the zigzag stabilimentum of *Argiope*, for example). It may be vertically or horizontally positioned, and is made up of the remains of prey, debris, cast skins of the spider and other bits and pieces, all woven in and attached to the web with thick white silk (see plate 4).

The spider takes up a position in the centre of this 'garbage line' with its legs stretched forwards and backwards or hunched up and is thus completely camouflaged. Unlike the cribellate spider *Uloborus* (see page 55), which rests in the centre of the hub with its legs outstretched and attempts to escape when disturbed, *Cyclosa* doggedly clings to the stabilimentum even when under extreme provocation.

C. *CYRTOPHORA* (TROPICAL TENT SPIDERS)

LIFESTYLE: Sedentary, web-bound
HABITAT: In built-up areas; in and up trees; on bushes and plants or in low base vegetation; near fresh water
SIZE: Medium-large to large. 8–20 mm
DIURNAL / NOCTURNAL

The abdomen of *Cyrtophora* is longer than it is wide, and high, with distinct, blunt tubercles. Colour varies from cream to black with white markings. Only one species, *C. cyrtricola*, has been described from the region.

The web, which is distinctive, is a globe of criss-crossed, tangled threads, commonly found in the middle of low base vegetation or

Tropical tent spider

in aloes and cacti, but also in and around suburban gardens. In the centre of the globe lies a horizontal or near-horizontal, fine orb web, sometimes pulled up slightly at the hub to form a tent-like sheet (see plate 6).

The spider hangs in negative geotaxis beneath the web, awaiting prey. The tangled threads and foundation lines of the web act as knockdown threads, and prey flying into them falls onto the horizontal orb web. The spider then moves to the prey and, through the web, bites and subdues it.

Rather like in the web of *Cyclosa*, there may be what looks like dotted masses of prey remains around the hub but these are mostly egg sacs disguised so as not to be disturbed.

Web of tropical tent spider

D. *CAEROSTRIS* (BARK SPIDERS)

LIFESTYLE: Sedentary, web-bound
HABITAT: In and up trees; in webs between trees; on or under bark
SIZE: Large. >16 mm
NOCTURNAL

The large bark spiders have horny or leathery protuberances on the abdomen, resembling the bark or thorns of trees. Their legs are covered with fine hair and when at rest fold in around the spider. The abdomen overhangs the carapace. The eight small eyes are on a tubercle on the front of the carapace.

31

Bark spider, at rest

At dusk, after establishing a long and sturdy bridge line, bark spiders construct a very large orb web which can span 1-1,5 m in diameter. The bridge line may measure up to 2 m between attachment points. At dawn the spider dismantles the web, leaving only the bridge line, and 'disappears' onto the nearest tree (see plate 7).

E. *NEMOSCOLUS* (STONE NEST SPIDER)

 ·

LIFESTYLE: Sedentary, web-bound
HABITAT: On rocks or in crevices of rocks; on bushes and plants or in low base vegetation; in, on or under grass
SIZE: Medium. 6–10 mm
DIURNAL

Web of stone nest spider with cornucopia

These are medium-sized spiders having an elliptical abdomen, the dorsal aspect of which has distinct white markings. In some species the abdomen extends past the spinnerets.

Nemoscolus constructs orb webs up to 20 cm in diameter, most often horizontally, in rocky grasslands, especially near rocky outcrops and low-hanging trees. A retreat is always constructed (see plate 10), varying in shape between species from an inverted cone to a spiral-like cornucopia. This shelter is constructed of tough silken threads into which are woven grains of sand, vegetable debris, and even shells of prey items. The retreat is secured above the hub of the web by tough silken threads which pull the centre of the web upwards into a cone shape. This retreat is also used for the egg sac and as an early nursery for the spiderlings.

F. *PYCNACANTHA* (HEDGEHOG SPIDER)

 ·

LIFESTYLE: Sedentary, web-bound
HABITAT: On bushes and plants or in low base vegetation; in, on or under grass
SIZE: Medium-large. 8–15 mm
DIURNAL

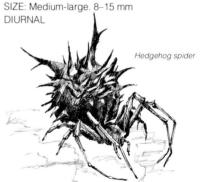

Hedgehog spider

The abdomen of the hedgehog spider is covered with numerous sharp spines, giving it the appearance of a hedgehog. It lives in grass; when at rest, with its legs pulled back, it resembles a grass seed. The smallish orb web is spun in among the grass and sometimes in woody bush.

32

1 Araneidae Argiope *sp. Banded garden spider (p. 28). A large, colourful spider, often seen hanging upside down in its orb web in grasslands and low base vegetation.*

2 Araneidae Gasteracantha *sp. Kite spider (p. 29). Generally brightly coloured, the kite spider has a hard abdomen which bears spiny protrusions.*

3 Araneidae Araneus *sp. Hairy field spider (p. 29). This spider spins a perfect orb web every evening.*

4 Araneidae Cyclosa *sp. Garbage line spider (p. 30). The spider hangs beneath some debris woven into its web.*

5 Araneidae Neoscona *sp. Hairy field spider (p. 29). Like her cousin, this spider spins a new web daily. (Both are illustrated on a flat surface to better show their shape.)*

6 Araneidae Cyrtophora *sp. Tropical tent spider (p. 31). The 'tent' effect of the pulled-up orb section of this spider's web is clearly visible here, where it is surrounded by attachment and knock-down threads.*

7 Araneidae Caerostris *sp. Bark spider (p. 31). During the day, this master of camouflage rests up against the bark of the tree nearest its web site.*

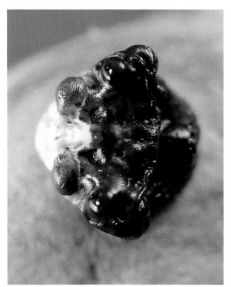 

8 Araneidae Aethriscus *sp. Bird dropping spider (p. 49). A clear illustration of the origin of this spider's common name.*

9 Araneidae Larinia *sp. Grass orb-web spider (p.50). This is one of the smallest spiders of the family Araneidae.*

10 Araneidae Nemoscolus *sp. Stone nest spider (p. 32). This distinctive web with its stone nest retreat fastened to the hub is diagnostic of the genus.*

11 Metidae Leucauge *sp. Silver vlei spider (p. 51). This spider resembles a miniature golden orb-web spider.*

12 Nephilidae Nephila senegalensis. *Golden orb-web spider (p. 52). A large and impressive-looking spider.*

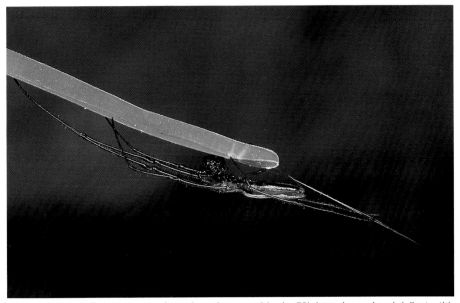

13 Tetragnathidae Tetragnatha *sp. Long-jawed water spider (p. 53). Long-legged and delicate, this spider builds its distinctive orb web near water. The web lacks a central hub.*

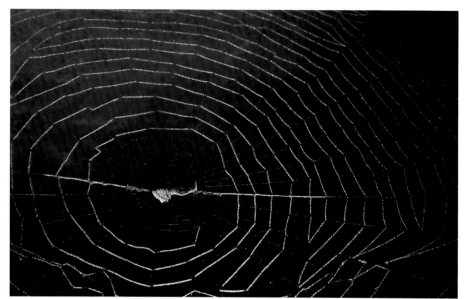

14 Uloboridae Uloborus *sp. Lace orb-web spider (p. 55). The uloborids are the only spiders in the world which have no poison glands whatsoever. Their web is built horizontally.*

15 Eresidae Gandanameno *sp. Velvet spider (p. 57). These large corpulent spiders live under rocks or the dead bark of trees, in tough but often messy silken tubes.*

16 Eresidae Stegodyphus dumicola. *Community nest spider (p. 59). Most often distinguished by the large and untidy nests they construct in trees, these spiders live in communities consisting mainly of immature and mature females.*

17 Agelenidae Olorunia sp. *Grass funnel-web spider (p. 62). This spider may be found in grasslands, especially in the early morning when the dew has settled on its web.*

18 Oecobiidae Uroctea *sp. Round-headed desert spider (p. 66). An inhabitant of the drier parts of the region, this spider lives under rocks and hunts at night.*

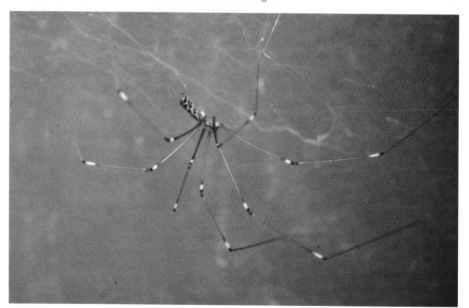

19 Pholcidae Smeringopus *sp. Daddy long legs spider (p. 69). The spider everyone knows: absolutely harmless to man and good to have in the home, where it preys on household pests.*

40

20 Deinopidae Menneus *sp. Net-casting spider (p. 72). At night, this spider holds a small, square web with the first two pairs of legs and hurls it, like a retarius, over passing prey.*

21 Anyphaenidae Amaurobioides africanus. *Sea-shore spider (p. 74). The smaller of the two intertidal spiders, here seen emerging from her waterproof silk retreat under a disused shell.*

41

22 Ammoxenidae Ammoxenus *sp. Sand-diver (p. 75). Extremely fast and agile, this spider, when disturbed, lives up to its common name by diving head-first into the sand.*

23 Desidae Desis formidabilis. *Long-jawed intertidal spider (p. 79). The formidable chelicerae, well illustrated here, are used by the spider to deal with its crustacean prey.*

42

24 Dysderidae Dysdera *sp. Giant-fanged six-eyed spider (p. 96). Not common in southern Africa, this is the only spider able to attack and kill the heavily armoured wood louse.*

25 Gnaphosidae. Mouse spider (p. 96). Found in homes, especially in sinks and baths, this spider is completely harmless and should be released out of doors.

26 Heteropodidae Palystes *sp. Rain spider (p. 97). The largest spider likely to be found in the home, its formidable size leads some people to think they have a tarantula in the house!*

27 Heteropodidae Palystes castaneus. *Rain spider (p. 98). The egg sac, known as a 'bag of leaves', serves as a nursery for the newly hatched spiderlings. It is guarded by the female.*

28 Heteropodidae Carparachne sp. Wheeling spider (p. 97). When threatened, carparachne folds in its legs and 'throws' itself down the side of the dune, cartwheeling at great speed.

29 Lycosidae Geolycosa sp. Trapdoor wolf spider (p. 100). Common all over South Afrca, wolf spiders may be seen scurrying over newly mown grass and found in compost pits.

45

30 Lycosidae Geolycosa *sp. Trapdoor wolf spider (p. 100). A rare picture of a wolf spider retreating into her burrow.*

31 Pisauridae Euprosthenops *sp. Nursery-web spider (p. 104). The web is typically built in disused mammal holes.*

32 Pisauridae Euprosthenops *sp. Nursery-web spider (p. 104). This spider carries its egg sac in its chelicerae and moves around on tiptoe in order to keep the eggs safely above the ground.*

33 Salticidae Salticus *sp. Jumping spider (p. 105). The two large anterior median eyes give this spider its anthropomorphic quality.*

34 Selenopidae Selenops *sp. Wall crab spider (p. 107). The 'flattie' is a master of camouflage and extremely agile.*

35 Salticidae Portia *sp. Jumping spider (p. 105). The male of this species is called the dandy for its elaborate pedipalps and the handsome black hairs on its body and upper legs.*

36 Scytodidae Syctodes *sp. Spitting spider (p. 106). Spitting spiders do spit! Here the female is seen carrying the egg sac in her chelicerae.*

37 Pisauridae Thalassius *sp. Fishing spider (p. 105). By moving the tarsus of one of the front legs, the fishing spider lures a minnow to the surface where it can be captured.*

Observations made of a captive specimen revealed that the egg sac is cone-shaped, with the apex hanging downwards from the web. The egg sac was constructed of light yellow silk.

G. *PARAPLECTANA* (LADYBIRD SPIDER)

LIFESTYLE: Sedentary, web-bound
HABITAT: On bushes and plants or in low base vegetation; in, on or under grass
SIZE: Small to medium. 3–8 mm
DIURNAL

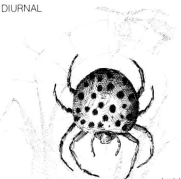

Ladybird spider

The abdomen of this orb-web spider is round and decorated with black spots on a bright yellow or red background. Not commonly seen but very distinctive, it is easy to recognize if found.

H. *CLADOMELEA* (AFRICAN BOLAS SPIDER)

LIFESTYLE: Free-running, plant-living
HABITAT: On bushes and plants or in low base vegetation; in, on or under grass
SIZE: Medium-large. 10–15 mm
NOCTURNAL

This genus is related to the bolas spiders of America and Australia. It is one of the excep-

African bolas spider, with bolas

tions to the rule in that it does not make an orb web. (Morphologically, however, it conforms to the set pattern for orb weavers, which is why it is included in this group.) Rather, it constructs a nest which it uses as a retreat by day, by pulling grass or leaves together with a binding of silken threads; within this framework egg sacs are constructed and attached.

At nightfall the spider moves to an upper portion of the nest and hangs from a bridge line. It produces a sticky droplet from its spinnerets, attaches this to a thread just long enough to suspend the droplet a few centimetres above the ground, and swings it around. The thread is held by the third leg or legs and not by the front legs as is the case with other bolas spiders. Any small insect that may fly into the path of the swinging ball is glued to it and reeled in by the spider overhead. Several of these droplets and lines may be constructed during one night.

I. *AETHRISCUS* (BIRD-DROPPING SPIDER)

LIFESTYLE: Sedentary, plant-living
HABITAT: On flowers or leaves
SIZE: Medium-large. 10–15 mm
DIURNAL

The bird-dropping spider has a smooth, glistening abdomen; as it rests on a leaf it resembles the wet excrement of a bird (see plate 8). It has been suggested that this mimicry is a defence mechanism to prevent the spider being picked off the leaf by foraging birds and

*Bird-dropping
spider, on leaf*

other predators; however, other writers suggest that certain butterflies and several types of fly are attracted to bird droppings for the salts they contain. Thus the mimicry serves two purposes, attracting prey and repelling predators.

Like the bolas spider, the bird-dropping spider does not make a web snare, but lies in ambush on the leaf.

J. *SINGA* (PYJAMA SPIDER)

 •

LIFESTYLE: Sedentary, web-bound
HABITAT: On bushes and plants or in low base vegetation; in, on or under grass
SIZE: Small to medium. 4–6 mm
DIURNAL / NOCTURNAL

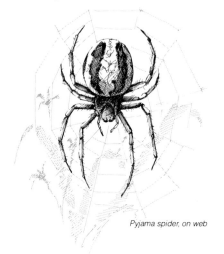

Pyjama spider, on web

These are some of the smallest members of the family. The abdomen is elliptical and shiny black, with longitudinal white stripes. The legs are short and stubby.

The small orb webs of these spiders are found near the ground in low base vegetation and grasslands.

K. *LARINIA* (GRASS ORB-WEB SPIDER)

 •

LIFESTYLE: Sedentary, web-bound
HABITAT: In, on or under grass
SIZE: Medium. 4–10 mm
DIURNAL / NOCTURNAL

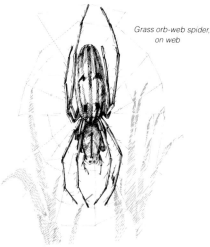

*Grass orb-web spider,
on web*

In *Larinia* the abdomen is more than twice as long as it is wide, and overlaps the cephalothorax. These are yellowish-brown spiders with dark longitudinal stripes along the dorsal aspect of the abdomen. The two front pairs of legs are characteristically held together and forwards and the two back legs together and backwards (see plate 9).

In the early morning the webs can be seen hanging in among the grass. When not in the web, *Larinia* may rest along grass stems like some members of the families Philodromidae and Thomisidae.

FAMILY: Metidae
SILVER VLEI SPIDERS AND CAVE ORB WEAVERS

COMMON GENERA: *Leucauge* (silver vlei spiders), *Meta* (cave orb weavers)

LIFESTYLE: Sedentary, web-bound
HABITAT: In and up trees; on bushes and plants or in low base vegetation; in, on or under grass; in forests; near fresh water; on flowers or leaves
SIZE: Medium to medium-large. 8–16 mm.
Female larger than male
DIURNAL / NOCTURNAL
POISON: Harmless
COLLECTING METHODS: Sweep-netting; beating; hand-to-jar

The metids were until recently placed with the long-jawed spiders (see page 52); however, neither of the two common genera have the typical, long slender jaws — the chelicerae are long but much more robust than those of the long-jawed spiders.

Leucauge, the silver vlei or orchard spider, is a brightly coloured spider resembling a miniature nephilid (see plate 11). Its abdomen has a silver sheen with green and red patterned markings and is longer than it is broad. *Meta* looks rather like a large theridiid: its abdomen is globose, with brownish-yellow markings, and its legs have obvious setae. Being an inhabitant of dark, damp places, the

Silver vlei spider

spider is seldom disturbed; its web consequently is often immaculate. A large, white, translucent egg sac is often seen hanging by a thread above the web. *Leucauge* may be distinguished from *Meta* by its colourful abdomen and by the presence of a fringe of curled hairs on the femur of its fourth leg.

Sexual dimorphism is marked, the male being only half the size of the female. The male *Leucauge* does, however, have the same bright colouring.

The webs of the metids are like those of the tetragnathids (see page 52) and are built mostly horizontally. *Meta* makes its web under overhanging boulders near streams, especially in mountainous terrain, and also in the entrances of caves and grottos. The web has the typical open hub of the long-jawed spiders. *Leucauge* spins a large, horizontal web in grass and reeds, nearly always near water and vleis. Unlike that of *Meta*, this web does have a central hub on which the spider rests, upside-down. An open space is clearly visible between the hub and the viscid catch zone of the outer web. In some species of *Leucauge* there is an accompanying barrier web built under the orb, in which the spider rests. The size of the web is very large for the size of the spider.

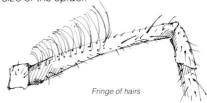
Fringe of hairs

FAMILY: Nephilidae
GOLDEN ORB-WEB SPIDERS

COMMON GENERA: *Nephila* (golden orb-web spiders), *Nephilengys* (hermit spiders)

LIFESTYLE: Sedentary, web-bound
HABITAT: In and up trees; in webs between trees;

on bushes and plants or in low base vegetation; in forests
SIZE: Large to very large. *Nephila* 25–>30 mm. *Nephilengys* >20 mm. Female much larger than male
DIURNAL
POISON: Harmless
COLLECTING METHOD: Hand-to-jar

Golden orb-web spider - note debris in web

The large, colourful golden orb-web spider is easily recognized both by its elongated, cylindrical abdomen which is marked in contrasting colours of black and yellow or white and yellow, and by its extremely long legs which give it a delicate look (see plate 12). The carapace is clothed with silver hairs covering most of the dark brown to black undertone. Two of the three species in the region, namely *Nephila senegalensis annulata* and *N. pilipes fenestrata,* have tufts of coarse hairs on the tibiae and femora of the first, second and fourth legs, and *N. senegalensis annulata* has clear yellow bands on its legs. The female *Nephila* is many times larger than the male, her body mass being as much as a thousand times more than his.

Nephilengys is slightly smaller in size than *Nephila*, and its distribution is limited to the eastern coastal regions. Most species are distinctive in having a bright yellow to orange-red sternum and their legs, like those of *Nephila senegalensis annulata*, are banded.

The golden orb-web spider hangs upside-down in the hub of its web, which can sometimes be recognized by the debris of old prey strung out in a line from the top to the bottom of the web and resembling a stabilimentum. Juveniles, both male and female, spin a complete orb, but as adults only the females spin the webs of strong, thick, golden silk. The adult spider does not spin a complete orb, leaving out the 'top part' of the orb, but because of all the attending threads it is difficult to notice that a section is missing. The whole construction is linked to branches and twigs with irregular, tough strands which also serve as knockdown lines. *Nephila* is easily disturbed, and will move away from the centre of its web if approached by an unfamiliar animal such as man. Kleptoparasites such as *Argyrodes* (see page 71) are often found in the orb webs of *Nephila*.

Nephilengys is known as the hermit spider as it makes a retreat to the side of its web. Its silk is white and its web, like that of *Nephila*, is not a full orb. In place of the missing portion is often the funnel-like retreat which may be seen in the forks of trees, in rock crevices and on walls. The spider emerges from the retreat only to catch prey.

FAMILY: **Tetragnathidae**
LONG-AND THICK-JAWED SPIDERS

COMMON GENERA: *Tetragnatha* (long-jawed water spiders), *Pachygnatha* (thick-jawed spiders), *Eucta* (long-tailed spiders)

  ·
 ·

LIFESTYLE: Sedentary, web-bound; free-running, ground-living
HABITAT: In webbing or scrapes under stones; on bushes and plants or in low base vegetation; in, on or under grass; in and under leaf litter and rotting logs; near fresh water

SIZE: *Tetragnatha* medium to medium-large, 6,7–15 mm (excluding chelicerae; leg span >30 mm). *Pachygnatha* medium to medium-large, 6–12 mm. *Eucta* medium to medium-large, 8,5–12 mm. Female slightly larger than male
DIURNAL / NOCTURNAL
POISON: Harmless
COLLECTING METHODS: Sweep-netting; beating; hand-to-jar

This family is represented by three genera most dissimilar in outward characteristics. *Tetragnatha* is distinctive in shape and colour. It has a long and slender body, with well-developed, elongated chelicerae and very long legs. Its general colour is light yellow to reddish-brown or grey, with silver and gold markings on the abdomen. The abdomen is usually broad at the base, tapering towards the spinnerets. One look at the chelicerae will confirm the diagnosis of this genus.

Pachygnatha has a much more globose abdomen, looking more like a large theridiid (see page 69) than like its near relatives. Its chelicerae are more robust and thickened, and its legs not quite as delicate and long as those of *Tetragnatha*. Its carapace is usually yellow, with an obscure border and a median band. In *Eucta* the abdomen projects a con-

siderable distance beyond the spinnerets and is very long and slender.

Tetragnatha, the long-jawed water spiders, are true orb weavers, making the typical wagon-wheel web. The web is constructed near or above a stream and is usually set at a slight angle or horizontal. Unique to this orb web is the absence of any central hub (see plate 13). On the web the spider hangs upside-down with its first and second legs stretched forwards. Unlike many of the other orb weavers, tetragnathids do not stay permanently on the web and may be found roaming freely or at rest on grass stems or twigs. At rest, six of the long spindly legs are stretched out, the first and second pairs to the front and the fourth to the back, while shorter third legs embrace the twig. The chelicerae of the male are longer than those of the female and in addition have a strong spur protruding from the inner frontal area. The spur is used to hold the female's jaws safely apart while mating takes place.

Pachygnatha are hunters and the adults do not build a web; however the young are known to build small orb webs. Not much is known of their behaviour other than that they are found under stones, especially in the vicinity of damp places, and under rotting logs and moist leaf litter.

Eucta is found in similar habitats to those of *Tetragnatha*.

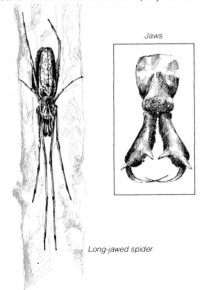
Jaws

Long-jawed spider

FAMILY: Theridiosomatidae
RAY SPIDERS
COMMON GENUS: *Baalzebub*

 ·   ·

LIFESTYLE: Sedentary, web-bound
HABITAT: In and up trees; on bushes and plants or in low base vegetation; in forests
SIZE: Tiny to very small. 0,5-2,5 mm
DIURNAL / NOCTURNAL
POISON: Harmless
COLLECTING METHODS: Hand-to-jar

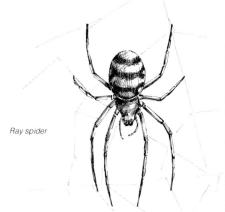

Ray spider

The theridiosomatids are very small spiders and can be recognized by the presence of pits on the front margin of the sternum in both sexes. In many ways, as their name suggests, they resemble small theridiids (see page 69). They have eight eyes in two rows, the carapace is pear-shaped, and the chelicerae are robust. The legs appear heavy for such a small spider. The abdomen is smoothly ovoid or has variously placed tubercles. The spider is usually uniform in colour, or has transverse silvery or white bands. When in their small webs with their legs pulled up alongside the body, these spiders look for all the world like a small seed caught up in the silk.

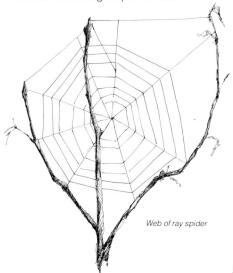

Web of ray spider

Theridiosomatids live almost exclusively in wet or humid areas like forests. Their webs are diverse but *Baalzebub* spins a complete orb. Indeed, the webs are their distinguishing feature and for many years they were mistakenly placed as a subfamily of the orb weavers on the basis of the appearance of their web. There is often a tension line more or less at right angles to the plane of the web and this the spider reels in to distort the orb into a conical form; when the spider releases the tension line, the web springs back to ensnare the prey.

FAMILY: Uloboridae
LACE ORB-WEB SPIDERS

COMMON GENERA: *Miagrammopes, Uloborus, Hyptiotes*

This family is unique in being the only family of spiders not to possess poison glands. They are cribellate spiders and build different kinds of webs which vary from a single-line web to an orb web.

A. *MIAGRAMMOPES* (SINGLE-LINE WEB SPIDERS)

 · ·

LIFESTYLE: Sedentary, web-bound
HABITAT: On bushes and plants or in low base vegetation
SIZE: Medium. 7–10 mm
NOCTURNAL
POISON: Nil
COLLECTING METHODS: Beating; hand-to-jar; night collecting

Also known as the tropical stick spider, *Miagrammopes* is small, with a long, narrow carapace and a cylindrical abdomen which is truncated above the spinnerets. The anterior eye row is reduced while the posterior eye row is recurved and widely spaced over the carapace.

*Eye pattern of
single line-web spider*

SIZE: Medium. 5–8 mm
DIURNAL / NOCTURNAL
POISON: Nil
COLLECTING METHODS: Sweep-netting;
beating; hand-to-jar

Lace orb-web spider

Miagrammopes is unique within the family in spinning a single-line web. The foundation is usually a horizontal strand between two branches or twigs. The length of the strand varies from one to three metres and only the section in the middle is covered with calamistrated silk: this is the catch web. Hanging in negative geotaxis, the spider grips the branch or a few threads attached to the branch with its hind legs. With its front legs it holds the foundation thread under tension. Although the different species differ in exact technique of prey capture, this involves a jerking and sudden sagging of the catch web as the prey touches it. As the prey is ensnared the spider rushes forwards along the line to devour it. *Miagrammopes* makes its web during the night, resting close to the branch during the day.

A smallish spider of a sedentary nature, *Uloborus* is characterized by its long front legs, rather humped abdomen and almost horizontal orb web (see plate 14). The common species *Uloborus plumipes*, frequently found in and around houses, has a brush of coarse, long hairs on the tibiae of the first leg in the female, and is often called the feather-legged spider. The eyes of *Uloborus* are arranged in two separated, curved rows.

This genus spins orb webs which are horizontal or obliquely inclined. The hub of the web is often meshed or strengthened with a stabilimentum. The spider sits in the centre of the web, legs stretched out along the strands of the stabilimentum. This renders it very hard to see unless it is disturbed. *Uloborus* builds its webs in low bushes, between objects near the ground and often in large cacti and succulents; they are also frequently found in and around outbuildings.

Single line-web spider, with web

B. *ULOBORUS* (LACE ORB-WEB SPIDERS)

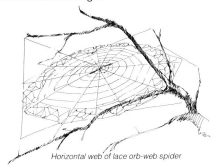

Horizontal web of lace orb-web spider

LIFESTYLE: Sedentary, web-bound
HABITAT: In built-up areas; in and up trees; on bushes and trees or in low base vegetation

C. *HYPTIOTES* (TRIANGLE-WEB SPIDERS)

 · ·

LIFESTYLE: Sedentary, web-bound
HABITAT: On bushes and plants or in low base vegetation
SIZE: Small to medium. 4–8 mm
DIURNAL / NOCTURNAL
POISON: Nil
COLLECTING METHODS: Sweep-netting; beating; hand-to-jar

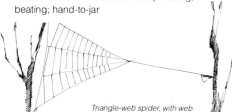

Triangle-web spider, with web

Not very common and rather inconspicuous because of their light brown ground colour, *Hyptiotes* are generally recognized in the field only by their webs. They normally rest close to a branch, using the body as a bridge between this and the triangle web. At rest, the spider resembles a dried-up bud and thus is often overlooked.

The abdomen is short, oval and humped, and is rather drab in colour. The legs are shorter and stouter than those of the other genera of this family. The eyes are diagnostic of this genus, the posterior row being placed well back on the carapace and being wider than the anterior row.

The web at first glance looks like a fragment of a complete orb web. It consists of only four radial lines attached to a holding thread and supporting a variable number of catch threads made of calamistrated silk. Pulling the holding thread tight but allowing some loose line to hang below, the spider awaits prey. When an insect becomes caught in the web, the spider lets go of the line, causing a 'spring action' which further ensnares the prey. So far only one species, *Hyptiotes akermani,* has been collected in South Africa, and this was from Natal.

T-Web Spiders

FAMILY: Amaurobiidae
LIGHT-EYED CRIBELLATE SPIDERS

 ·

 ·

LIFESTYLE: Sedentary, ground-living
HABITAT: In webbing, scrapes or free-running, under stones; on open ground; on rocks or in crevices of rocks; in and under leaf litter and rotting logs; in forests; in caves
SIZE: Medium to medium-large. 6–16 mm
NOCTURNAL
POISON: Harmless
COLLECTING METHODS: Hand-to-jar; night collecting; pitfall trap; sifting; rock turning

SUBFAMILY: Phyxelidinae

COMMON GENERA: *Malaika, Matundua, Namaquarachne, Phyxelida, Themacrys, Vidole, Xeviosa* (the genera listed under Dictynidae in Lawrence (1964) are now transferred to this family)

SUBFAMILY: Macrobuninae

COMMON GENERA: *Chresiona* (ecribellate), *Macrobunus* (ecribellate), *Obatala*

Light-eyed cribellate spider

A family of rather drab, ground-living spiders resembling the gnaphosids (see page 96) in general appearance, with some genera not unlike the agelenids (see page 62). These are three-clawed, cribellate (with two exceptions) spiders and are in fact the commonest cribellate spiders in southern Africa. All genera in the subfamily Phyxelidinae have a distinctly divided cribellum, while two of the genera in Macrobuninae are ecribellate.

The carapace is longer than it is wide, with the eyes (light in colour in most species) arranged in two rows. The abdomen is oval, with ill-defined patterns dorsally. The legs are fairly long, especially in the males. The metatarsi of the first leg of the males of some species are strongly modified.

The amaurobiids are typical representatives of southern African crypto-fauna living in cool, damp places. However, some species (eg. *Vidole*) are found in the drier parts of the country and a few species (eg. *Phyxelida* and *Themacrys*) are found in caves. Three species have been recorded from open thorn bush and savanna.

They construct irregular, tangled webs which are easily seen under stones, in cracks of rocks or trees and under rotten logs on the forest floor. The web, made of bluish cribellate silk, has a typical funnel-like appearance in some species.

Most of these spiders are nocturnal.

Modified metatarsi

Face

FAMILY: Eresidae

VELVET SPIDERS

COMMON GENERA: *Dresserus, Gandanomeno, Paradonea, Adonea, Stegodyphus, Seothyra*

LIFESTYLE: Sedentary, web-bound; free-running, ground-living; sedentary, ground-living; sedentary, plant-living
DIURNAL / NOCTURNAL

The eresids are corpulent spiders, with the carapace bluntly rounded in front, and they usually have thick, short legs. They all possess a cribellum and calamistrum. The median eyes are set close to each other, while both pairs of lateral eyes are set far apart from them. There is usually sexual dimorphism, with the males smaller and different in colour.

Behaviourally, the eresids can be both arboreal and terrestrial.

A. *DRESSERUS* (HORNED VELVET SPIDERS), *GANDANAMENO* (COMMON VELVET SPIDERS)

  ·

HABITAT: *Dresserus* in webbing or scrapes under stones; *Gandanameno* on or under bark
SIZE: Medium to very large. 12– >30 mm. Female usually larger than male
POISON: Harmless
COLLECTING METHODS: *Dresserus* hand-to-jar; pitfall trap; rock turning. *Gandanameno* hand-to-jar

Dresserus and *Gandanameno* (previously listed as *Eresus*) are black or dark brown to reddish-brown and are covered in fine hairs, giving them a velvety appearance. The cephalic area in both males and females is weakly raised, with the fovea present as a circular pit. *Dresserus* has a cribellum which is tri- or quadripartite, and the males have

Quadripartite cribellum

Bipartite cribellum

horn-like tubercles on the edge of the carapace. *Gandanameno* has a cribellum which is bipartite.

Species of *Dresserus* are usually found under stones, where they build a messy, bluish-white, shroud-like retreat of loosely woven silk with grains of sand imbedded in it. The retreat hangs like a pendulous sac when the stone is lifted. These spiders are loath to emerge from their web and have to be gently prized out. Sluggish and generally not aggressive, they are easy to capture.

Gandanameno is usually found under the loose bark or in the crevices and old knot holes of trees. They build a funnel-like web into a crevice, with the entrance to the web sheltering under a tarpaulin-like, flat and solid web, anchored to the substrate by scalloped, tough, silken threads. Well-established females in old trees or trees with loosened bark may present a veritable maze of webbing and tunnels, making them very difficult to find and collect (see plate 15).

Both genera can be found throughout southern Africa.

Female velvet spider

B. *PARADONEA, ADONEA* (DECORATED VELVET SPIDERS)

  ·

HABITAT: In webbing, scrapes or free-running, under stones; in semi-arid desert
SIZE: Medium to very large. 12–30 mm. Female usually larger than male
POISON: Harmless
COLLECTING METHODS: Hand-to-jar; pitfall trap; rock turning

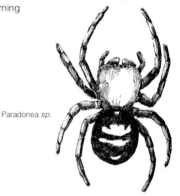

Paradonea sp.

The decorated velvet spiders are large spiders, although the males are smaller than the females. *Paradonea* is black with white markings on the abdomen, while the smaller *Adonea* is usually brown to black with white spots on the abdomen. In both the carapace shows a high cephalic portion, strongly sloping behind, with the abdomen oval to roundish in shape. In *Paradonea* the anterior lateral eyes are set on prominent tubercles, which are absent in *Adonea*. In *Paradonea* the first leg is much longer than the fourth, while in *Adonea* the first leg is not much longer than the fourth.

Little is known about the behaviour of *Paradonea*, which is described only from Runtu on the Okavango River. *Adonea* constructs its nest under stones. Its distribution is given as Namibia, little Namaqualand, parts of the Cape Province (including Worcester), the north-western parts of Transvaal (Marico area), and Pretoria.

C. *STEGODYPHUS* (COMMUNITY NEST SPIDERS)

   ·

HABITAT: In and up trees; in webs between trees; on bushes and plants or in low base vegetation
SIZE: Medium to very large. 10–20 mm. Female usually larger than male
POISON: Harmless
COLLECTING METHODS: Beating; hand-to-jar

The community nest spiders are medium-sized, and greyish-brown to fawn, usually with patterns on the abdomen. The males are smaller and more brightly coloured than the females. The carapace is slightly raised and distinctively clothed in white hairs. (In *Stegodyphus dumicola* a triangular pattern is present between the eyes; this pattern is formed by rows of white hairs.)

These spiders are most often noticed because of the large and untidy nests they construct in trees, usually *Acacia* (see plate 16). A large number of females, males and juveniles live together in one nest. They use cribellate silk to spin these nests, which consist of a retreat of numerous tunnels and chambers in which the spiders live, and a web which is used to catch prey. These catch webs, set out at various angles to the retreat, are attached to nearby branches. Prey that lands on the catch web is killed by a party of spiders and dragged into or close to the retreat, to be consumed by the community.

A genus belonging to the family Dictynidae, *Archaedictyna* (see page 67), may sometimes be found living in harmony with the eresids in the community web.

Stegodyphus is found throughout southern Africa. In areas like the Orange Free State where trees are scarce, they attach their nests to fences.

D. *SEOTHYRA* (BUCKSPOOR SPIDERS)

   ·

HABITAT: On or under sand; in burrows; in semi-arid desert
SIZE: Medium to medium-large. 8–15 mm. Female usually larger than male
POISON: Little is known about their poison, but according to people from Namibia, the Bushmen used the spider's venom on their arrow heads to kill prey
COLLECTING METHODS: Males, pitfall traps; females and juveniles, hand-to-jar; digging

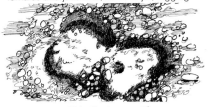
Web of buckspoor spider

The buckspoor spiders are known only from southern Africa. They are common in the more arid regions of Namibia, the Cape Province and the Transvaal, and live in a hole in the ground which is covered by a silk sheet resembling the spoor of a buck.

Seothyra is reddish-brown to fawn, with some species having faint markings on the abdomen. Distinctive of this genus are the very small posterior spinnerets, which are scarcely half the length of the inferior ones. These spiders are smaller than the other eresids, and distinct sexual dimorphism exists in that the male differs completely from the female in size, shape and colour.

Seothyra is subterranean. It digs a tubular retreat, covering it with a two- or four-lobed carpet of silk and sand that resembles a buck

Community nest spiders, in web

spoor. This 'spoor' is most easily detected in the early morning or late afternoon when the sun throws long shadows on the ground. Once recognized, many such nests may be found in one area.

The spider positions herself in negative geotaxis under the web, grabbing from underneath any prey walking over it. The *Seothyra* male runs around freely on the surface, mimicking the ants that live in the vicinity.

FAMILY: Filistatidae
EIGHT-EYED TUNNEL SPIDERS

GENERA: South African specimens yet to be described but related to South American genera *Pikelinia* and *Filistatoides*

LIFESTYLE: Sedentary, ground-living
HABITAT: In webbing under stones; on rocks or in crevices of rocks
SIZE: Medium to large. 8–30 mm
NOCTURNAL
POISON: Harmless
COLLECTING METHODS: Hand-to-jar; rock turning

Light yellow to brown cribellate spiders without any distinctive markings, the eight-eyed tunnel spiders are similar in general appearance to the amaurobiids (see page 56). The carapace does, however, have a distinctive shape, and the eight eyes are massed in a small group in the centre front of this carapace on a small tubercle. They have long legs, especially in the male, the first pair being the longest. Ventrally, the labium is fused to the sternum (a good taxonomic tool) but the cribellum is very difficult to see and can easily be missed. The spinnerets are more ventral than terminal.

These are sedentary spiders, living their lives in rather untidy cribellate webs in the natural crevices of rocks and under rocks. The tubular webs are conspicuous, often being built up and over the upper surface of the rock. Because of its sticky nature the web is soon encrusted with dust.

These spiders are recorded from Namibia and the northern Cape.

FAMILY: Segestriidae
SIX-EYED TUNNEL SPIDERS

COMMON GENUS: *Ariadna* (incorporates those species previously listed under *Segestriella*)

LIFESTYLE: Sedentary, web-bound
HABITAT: In built-up areas; on or under bark; in webbing, under stones; on rocks or in crevices of rocks; in and under leaf litter and rotting logs
SIZE: Medium-large to large. 12–30 mm
NOCTURNAL
POISON: Harmless
COLLECTING METHOD: Hand-to-jar

Segestriids have six eyes closely grouped in the centre front of a cephalothorax that is longer than it is wide and generally dark brown. Most species in our region are rather drab spiders, uniformly coloured in shades of brown, with the long, oval abdomen sometimes a greyish-brown. The abdomen is rather bulbous and tends to droop over to one side when the spider is removed from its retreat; this is because the pedicel is very thin and weak. Characteristic of this family is the third pair of legs, which is directed forwards instead of backwards as in most other spiders,

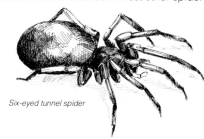

Six-eyed tunnel spider

and that they breathe through four tracheal spiracles, visible under moderate magnification on either side of the epigastric furrow.

Nocturnal and sedentary, they spend most of their lives in a tubular retreat of tough white silk under rocks, fallen logs, in crevices of rocks and often in the rolled-up dead leaves of succulent plants. In some species, single lines of silken thread radiate from the mouth of the tube, acting as trip lines for passing prey. The spider can be seen waiting within the tube with the first three pairs of legs projecting slightly.

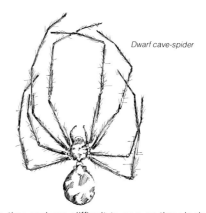

Dwarf cave-spider

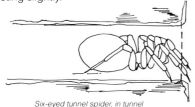

Six-eyed tunnel spider, in tunnel

FAMILY: Telemidae
DWARF CAVE-SPIDERS

COMMON GENUS: *Cangoderces*

LIFESTYLE: Sedentary, web-bound
HABITAT: In caves
SIZE: Tiny to very small. <2 mm
POISON: Harmless
COLLECTING METHODS: Hand-to-jar; pooter

The telemids are tiny, six-eyed spiders, always found in dark places. Some species have lost most of their coloration and present a pale yellow colour that is almost translucent. *Cangoderces* is pale, with only the articulations of the leg segments, the sternum and the chelicerae a light reddish-brown. They have a well-chitinized carapace and abdomen.

The cephalothorax and abdomen of telemids appear roundish from above, the abdomen itself being quite globose. The legs are long and slender, well covered with setae, and point outwards and forwards. The eyes

are tiny and are difficult to see as they lack pigmentation. They are set in three widely separated groups of two, forming a recurved line on slightly raised tubercles.

Virtually nothing is known about the behaviour of these small spiders. Specimens collected in the Cango Caves were found in small webs spun in crevices in the rock wall, always about 45 cm above the ground.

FAMILY: Zodariidae
ARMOURED SPIDERS

COMMON GENERA: *Cydrela* (tube-living zodariids), *Caesetius* (sandswimmers), *Diores* (ant-like zodariids)

LIFESTYLE: Free-running, ground-living; sedentary, ground-living
HABITAT: In webbing, scrapes or free-running, under stones; on or under sand; on open ground; in burrows; in semi-arid desert; in association with insects
SIZE: Medium to medium-large. 6,5–15 mm
DIURNAL / NOCTURNAL
POISON: Harmless
COLLECTING METHODS: Hand-to-jar; night collecting; pitfall trap; rock turning

Armoured spider

The zodariids are eight-eyed hunting spiders very diverse in general appearance. In some genera the epidermis of the carapace and legs is thick and tough and looks like armour. The legs are usually similar in length and thickness. The anterior spinnerets of zodariids are usually the longest and are situated close together; their unique shape provides a useful taxonomic tool. The posterior and median spinnerets are short. This configuration can be seen under moderate magnification.

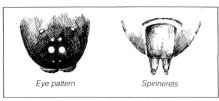

Eye pattern	*Spinnerets*

In *Cydrela* and *Caesetius* the body is large and robust; these are medium to large spiders, but *Diores* is more delicate, mimicking the ants among which it lives.

Some species of *Cydrela* make a tube-like burrow with a lid, like those of the trapdoor spiders (see page 115). *Caesetius* is found under stones and is said to make a sac-like nest which may hang down like a bag when the stone is lifted. Some *Caesetius* are adapted to living in sand and if threatened can rapidly burrow head-first into the sand.

Diores is diurnal and can be seen running furiously back and forth with the ants. It spins a bag-like retreat under rocks, on rocks near the ant colony or on the ant mound itself. The retreat is often camouflaged with pebbles and debris, and at night the spider takes refuge in this hideaway. Some authors have likened the retreat to an igloo.

Sheet Web Spiders

FAMILY: **Agelenidae**

FUNNEL-WEB SPIDERS

COMMON GENERA: *Olorunia* (grass funnel-web spiders, incorporates African species previously listed under *Agelena)*, *Tegenaria* (house funnel-web spiders)

 ·   ·

LIFESTYLE: Sedentary, web-bound
HABITAT: In built-up areas; on bushes and plants or in low base vegetation; in, on or under grass
SIZE: Medium to medium-large. 7–13 mm
DIURNAL
POISON: Harmless
COLLECTING METHOD: Hand-to-jar

Female grass funnel-web spiders, *Olorunia*, live permanently on a large, sheet-like web with a funnel retreat made close to the substrate (see plate 17). In the field they may be identified firstly by their webs and, once in the hand, by their resemblance to wolf spiders (see page 99) in size and colour. They are usually dark sooty grey to mottled brown, with the abdomen decorated with a reddish-brown folium and a series of yellow to white spots or bands. The legs are long and narrow towards the extremities and are hairy, with spines mostly long and aculeate. The carapace is long and narrowed in front, with the eyes, which are nearly equal in size, situated in two procurved rows. The abdomen is oval and

Funnel-web spider

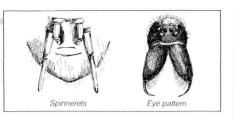

Spinnerets   Eye pattern

LIFESTYLE: Sedentary, web-bound
HABITAT: in and up trees; in webs between trees; on rocks or in crevices of rocks; on bushes and plants or in low base vegetation; in forests
SIZE: Tiny to small. 1–6 mm
DIURNAL / NOCTURNAL
POISON: Harmless
COLLECTING METHODS: Sweep-netting; beating; hand-to-jar; tullgren funnel; sifting; pooter

tapers posteriorly. Characteristic are the two elongated and slender posterior spinnerets, tapering at the ends and visible from above. The agelenids have three claws.

In *Tegenaria* the eyes are in two straight rows and the apical segment of the posterior pair of spinnerets is shorter.

Olorunia is most easily found in the early morning when the dew has settled on the web, making it opaque. The web consists of a flat, slightly concave silk mat (40-60 cm wide) with a funnel-shaped retreat at one end. The retreat is open-ended, allowing the spider to escape when threatened. Often the narrowed tunnel portion abuts a grass tuft or a gravel mound, or is built in and around rocks and may even disappear beneath them.

Prey landing on the silk mat quickly brings the spider to the entrance of the retreat; the spider may be seen orienting itself towards the prey, then dashing across the mat to capture it and drag it back into the retreat.

Tegenaria, the house funnel-web spider, contains the cosmopolitan domesticated species. *Tegenaria domestica*, a large introduced species, has been found in houses in Cape Town.

FAMILY: Cyatholipidae
MIDGET SHEET-WEB WEAVERS

COMMON GENERA: *Cyatholipus, Ilisoa, Isicabu, Ulwembua*

Midget sheet-web weaver

The cyatholipids are very small, three-clawed spiders resembling very small theridiids (see page 69). The carapace is convex, heart-shaped to oval and is usually heavily sclerotized. The clypeus is vertical and may be straight or mildly concave. The eyes are in two rows and from above the anterior row appears strongly recurved while the posterior row is either straight or slightly recurved. The lateral eyes of both rows are on a low tubercle and are contiguous.

In *Cyatholipus* the abdomen is usually spherical but sometimes ovoid, and extends beyond the spinnerets. There are rows of stout bristles dorsally which extend to the sides and posteriorly. The legs of some species are long and slender and in most are well-armed with spines. In others the legs may be relatively shorter and sparsely covered with fine hairs.

In *Iliosa* the abdomen is ovoid and shows the same unique presence of abdominal bristles. All species in this genus have slender legs covered sparsely with fine hairs.

In *Isicabu* the abdomen is triangular and extends beyond the spinnerets. It may be weakly sclerotized. The legs are very long and slender and are usually covered with long, fine hairs.

The abdomen of *Ulwembua* is triangular and also extends beyond the spinnerets. It is sclerotized around the spinnerets and in front of the epigastric furrow. The legs are very long and have scattered, short spines.

Although recently a number of new species have been described, the family as a whole is poorly known. They build small, horizontal sheet webs between trees and bushes and within the branches, and have also been found in low vegetation and between boulders. The spider hangs beneath the sheet web, similar to the linyphiids (see page 64), and is solitary.

Most species are forest dwellers, 11 of the 14 known species being recorded from wet temperate, montane or subtropical forests.

FAMILY: Hahniidae
COMB-TAILED SPIDERS

COMMON GENERA: *Hahnia, Muizenbergia* (incorporates those species previously listed under *Scotussa*)

LIFESTYLE: Sedentary, web-bound
HABITAT: On open ground; in, on or under grass; in and under leaf litter and rotting logs; near fresh water; on the seashore
SIZE: Small. 2–6 mm
DIURNAL / NOCTURNAL
POISON: Harmless
COLLECTING METHODS: Hand-to-jar; tullgren funnel; sifting; pooter

The comb-tailed spiders are small spiders. They may be distinguished from other families by the spinnerets, which are arranged in a single, transverse row; when seen from above, they appear like the teeth of a comb protruding from the abdomen. The carapace is longer than it is wide and is narrowed in the cephalic region. The eight eyes are equal in size and arranged in two procurved rows. The abdomen usually shows a chevron pattern,

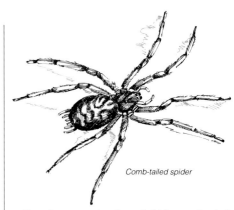
Comb-tailed spider

with colours varying from light brown to dark brownish-black.

The web of the comb-tailed spider is delicate and most often built close to the ground. Commonly found in moist areas, in moss and cultivated fields, it is most easily seen in the early morning when the dew has settled on it. The spider is found under the web or to the side, next to some attachment.

Some species are found along the seashore, sometimes within the splash zone but never below it. Some writers include the hahniids with the intertidal spiders.

FAMILY: Linyphiidae
HAMMOCK, SHEET OR DOME-WEB SPIDERS; DWARF OR MONEY SPIDERS

POISON: Family as a whole is harmless
COLLECTING METHODS: Beating; hand-to-jar; tullgren funnel; sifting; pooter

Dome-web spider

SUBFAMILY: Linyphiinae

HAMMOCK, SHEET OR DOME-WEB SPIDERS

COMMON GENERA: *Lepthyphantes, Linyphia, Microlinyphia, Mecynidis, Meioneta*

LIFESTYLE: Sedentary, web-bound
HABITAT: On open ground; on rocks or in crevices of rocks; on bushes and plants or in low base vegetation; in, on or under grass; in and under leaf litter and rotting logs
SIZE: Very small to small. <2–4 mm
DIURNAL / NOCTURNAL

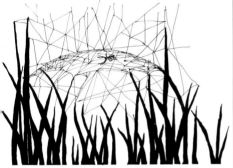

Web of dome-web spider

A large family of very small spiders often resembling the males of the family Theridiidae (see page 69). The eyes are in two rows, with the anterior median eyes often darker than the rest. The abdomen tends to be globose and usually shiny black to brown, with some species having white markings. In most of the species the legs are relatively long and thin.

Linyphiids are often overlooked because of their small size and their secluded, sedentary behaviour. Most of them build a distinctive web, which often takes the form of a small sheet web, and which may or may not have strands of silken thread above it, built close to the ground. Some species that live in low base vegetation build a superstructure above the sheet, with several central draw lines pulling the centre of the web up slightly. This has given rise to the common name 'hammock

spider'. The webs are best seen when covered with early-morning dew.

The spider lives and runs on the underside of the web, which is used as a food trap. When prey falls on the sheet it is grabbed and pulled through the web to be devoured below.

SUBFAMILY: Erigoninae

DWARF OR MONEY SPIDERS

COMMON GENERA: *Erigone, Erigonopsis, Ostearius*

LIFESTYLE: Sedentary, web-bound; free-running, ground-living
HABITAT: On bushes and plants or in low base vegetation; in and under leaf litter and rotting logs; on the seashore
SIZE: Tiny to very small. <2 mm
DIURNAL / NOCTURNAL

Most dwarf spiders are less than 2 mm long. They can be distinguished from the Linyphiinae in having shorter, more robust legs and being very dark brown to black, and shiny. In some species the males have extravagant and gross deformations of the front portion of the carapace.

Dwarf spiders make tiny, flat sheet webs close to the soil, often in depressions made by animal hooves, etc. Some live under debris and leaf litter, while a species of *Erigonopsis* is found in the unoccupied worm tubes between the tidal marks on the shores of the Cape Peninsula.

Ostearius melanopygius is a cosmopolitan species commonly found in southern Africa.

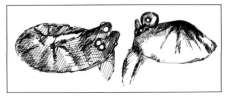

Detail of carapace deformations of dwarf spider

FAMILY: Oecobiidae
DWARF ROUND-HEADED SPIDERS

COMMON GENERA: *Oecobius* (dwarf round-headed house spiders), *Uroecobius* (dwarf round-headed rock spiders), *Uroctea* (round-headed desert spiders)

 ·   ·

LIFESTYLE: Free-running, ground-living
HABITAT: *Oecobius* in built-up areas; *Uroecobius* on rocks or in crevices of rocks; *Uroctea* in webbing, scrapes or free-running, under stones; in semi-arid desert
SIZE: *Oecobius* very small, 1,5-2,5 mm. *Uroecobius* very small, 1,4–2 mm. *Uroctea* medium to medium-large, 6–12 mm. Female slightly larger than male
DIURNAL / NOCTURNAL
POISON: Harmless
COLLECTING METHODS: Hand-to-jar; pooter; rock turning

Oecobius is very small and pale coloured, and is found in and around dwellings, either under its star-shaped web or indoors on table tops and along skirting boards (the Latin name 'oecobii' means 'living at home'). The carapace is wider than it is long, and round in shape, hence the common name. *Oecobius* can easily be recognized by the position of the eyes, which are closely grouped near the

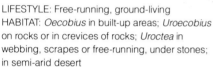

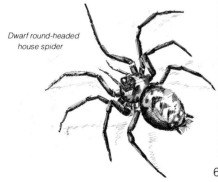

Dwarf round-headed house spider

centre of the carapace and situated on a slight tubercle. The legs are held in a characteristic star-like fashion around the body.

Uroecobius, also a very small spider, is found on rocks and rock faces (see plate 18). To the naked eye it resembles its urban cousin in shape, but may be differentiated from *Oecobius* under a microscope when it will be seen that it lacks a cribellum and has a different eye pattern. These spiders are easily overlooked unless disturbed.

Uroctea is a much larger spider. Found only in the more arid regions of our country, it is darker in colour than its relatives, with variable colour markings on the abdomen. The rounded carapace shows a clypeal snout and the hairy abdomen seems to overlap the carapace, giving it a strange hunched-back appearance.

Round-headed spiders may be distinguished from other spider families by their large, two-jointed anal tubercle with its double fringe of curled hairs which can be easily seen with the aid of a magnifying glass.

Oecobius builds a tiny, white, star-like web about 30 mm in diameter over crevices on any flat surfaces or corners within a house. The spider when waiting for prey can be seen sitting beneath its web on the substrate with its back to the web. The web is thus used both as a catch web and as a retreat. If disturbed the spider will dash away with speed.

If prey (usually small ants) disturb the foundation lines of the web, the spider dashes out and enswathes the prey with silk by running rapidly around it in an anticlockwise direction. It is the prevalence of ants in its diet that gives *Oecobius* its Afrikaans name 'miervreter'.

The web of *Uroecobius* is also white and star-like in shape and is built over crevices and holes on rock surfaces. This genus catches its prey in the same manner as does *Oecobius*.

The much larger *Uroctea* spins a characteristic, easily recognizable web under stones in dry, arid regions. This fine, multi-layered, inverted structure features a flat base built against the stone, a dome-shaped vault built against the ground and a round, scalloped

Round-headed desert spider

edge fastened with anchor threads to the stone. Frequently, small objects like pebbles and other bits of debris are attached to the silk threads.

FAMILY: Symphytognathidae

MIDGET SPIDERS

COMMON GENUS: *Symphytognatha*

  ·   ·

LIFESTYLE: Sedentary, web-bound; free-running, ground-living
HABITAT: In and under leaf litter and rotting logs; in forests
SIZE: Tiny to very small. <2 mm
DIURNAL / NOCTURNAL
POISON: Harmless
COLLECTING METHODS: Hand-to-jar; pitfall trap; tullgren funnel; sifting; pooter

Midget spider

As New Zealand author Forster says, 'If you can think small enough, they are easy to find!' These tiny, yellow-brown spiders have their

chelicerae fused at the base. The palp of the female is absent or reduced to one segment. They have four or six eyes (*Symphytognatha* has six) arranged in diads or triads on a pronounced prominent carapace. Booklungs are absent.

Little is known about these spiders in southern Africa, and they are rarely found. Typically cryptozoic, they inhabit high-humidity areas like the forest floor and under damp leaf litter. Although they never measure more than 2 mm in length, it is amazing to see their small sheet webs stretched across the mossy ground cover and on the moist, moss-covered lower trunks of trees in damp forest areas. Although some construct orb webs, others have lost the ability to be web-bound.

Scaffold Web And Lace Web Spiders

FAMILY: Dictynidae

HACKLED-WEB SPIDERS

COMMON GENERA: *Archaedictyna*, *Dictyna*, *Shango*, *Mashimo* (the genera listed under Dictynidae in Lawrence (1964) are now placed in the Amaurobiidae)

 ·   ·

LIFESTYLE: Sedentary, web-bound
HABITAT: In and up trees; on bushes and plants or in low base vegetation; in forests
SIZE: Small to medium. 3–8 mm
DIURNAL
POISON: Harmless
COLLECTING METHODS: Sweep-netting; beating; hand-to-jar; pooter

The dictynids are small spiders having a wide cribellum and a uniserate calamistrum, but are generally recognized only by their unique webs. The abdomen may slightly overlap the carapace and is usually decorated with light

Hackled-web spider

and dark patterns. The carapace is distinctly high and usually clothed in white hairs. The eyes are arranged in two straight rows and are almost the same size. The anterior median eyes are dark and the rest of the eyes appear pearly white. The chelicerae are typically long and indented.

Most hackled-web spiders seem to be solitary, constructing irregular webs as traps to catch prey. Most often these small webs are positioned on plants at the terminal points of branches and dried twigs, and a few are found on walls. A framework of simple dry lines is constructed, then criss-crossed with calamistrated silk to form a symmetrical sheet or lattice network. Within the web the female constructs a small retreat for herself, and in summer the male may sometimes be found there with her.

The dictynids are common on plants throughout southern Africa.

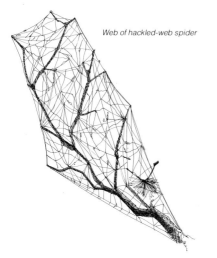

Web of hackled-web spider

FAMILY: **Nesticidae**

SCAFFOLD-WEB SPIDERS

COMMON GENUS: *Nesticella*

 ·   ·

LIFESTYLE: Sedentary, web-bound
HABITAT: In webbing under stones; in and under leaf litter and rotting logs; in forests; in caves
SIZE: Small. 3–5 mm
DIURNAL / NOCTURNAL
POISON: Harmless
COLLECTING METHOD: Hand-to-jar

Scaffold-web spider

Small spiders resembling those of the family Theridiidae (see page 69), but with more robust legs. The first pair of legs is significantly longer than the other three pairs. The diameter of the legs is much the same throughout their length. The embolus of the palp of the male is loosely arranged with processes on the cymbium, unlike the compact embolus of the male theridiids.

Living in dark, dank places and under damp stones, some species have lost their pigmentation; this is first seen in the eyes, which are often rudimentary. The abdomen is greyish and pale or yellowish-white; in some species it has short, 'fluffy' brown hairs.

Little is known about the behaviour of these small spiders. They make a fine web under damp stones or in dark, dank places and are adapted to life in caves. The web is similar to those made by *Steatoda* (see page 71), hence the family's common name.

The egg sac is pale brown and is carried by the female, attached to the spinnerets in the same fashion as the wolf spiders (see page 99).

FAMILY: Pholcidae

DADDY LONG LEGS SPIDERS

COMMON GENERA: *Pholcus* and *Smeringopus* (daddy long legs spiders), *Spermophora* (short-bellied cellar spiders)

 ·

LIFESTYLE: Sedentary, web-bound
HABITAT: In built-up areas; on rocks or in crevices of rocks; in and under leaf litter and rotting logs; in disused holes; in caves
SIZE: Medium-large. 8–15 mm (leg span up to 30 mm)
DIURNAL / NOCTURNAL
POISON: Harmless
COLLECTING METHOD: Hand-to-jar

Daddy long legs spider

These are delicate spiders with very thin, long legs — as much as four times as long as the body — that lack setae (see plate 19). *Pholcus* and *Smeringopus* have a cylindrical abdomen with chevron markings, while *Spermophora* has a more globular abdomen. The eye patterns of *Pholcus* and *Smeringopus* are very similar: there are two sets, each of three contiguous eyes, on either side of the carapace, raised on slight tubercles, with two smaller anterior median eyes in the centre front of the carapace. In *Spermophora* the anterior median eyes are absent.

These long-legged, often seen spiders spin a simple web of long threads criss-cross-ing in an irregular fashion. Mostly they are seen in dark corners of garages, disused habitations, damp places and often in the disused holes of mammals. The webs are thus frequently covered with dust and debris.

The spider hangs upside-down towards the centre of the web; sometimes, however, the web appears to have a more concentrated section away from the centre, and this is where the spider will be found. The apparent size of the web can sometimes be misleading as offspring setting up home nearby create a sort of continuation of the main web.

Pholcids, unlike the violin spiders (see page 99), remain on their webs unless torn away from them when supporting structures such as garage rubble or building material are moved. When detached from the web they appear to bounce along the floor as they search for a hiding place. If the web is touched or blown upon, the spider will shake itself and the web violently, or swing itself around rapidly. The vibration it thus sets up renders the spider invisible, or at least an inconspicious blur.

The female carries the eggs, which are loosely joined together with agglutinating silk, in her chelicerae.

Preying on ants and other household pests, these spiders are to be encouraged in the home, certainly never killed.

FAMILY: Theridiidae

COMB-FOOTED SPIDERS

COMMON GENERA: *Argyrodes*, *Latrodectus*, *Steatoda*, *Theridion*

 ·
     ·

LIFESTYLE: Sedentary, web-bound
HABITAT: In built-up areas; in and up trees; in webbing under stones; on rocks or in crevices of rocks; on bushes and plants or in low base

vegetation; in, on or under grass; in and under leaf litter and rotting logs; in forests; in other spiders' webs; in disused holes
SIZE: Small to medium. 4–10 mm
DIURNAL / NOCTURNAL
POISON: Venomous. *Latrodectus indistinctus*, the black button spider, is one of the most dangerous spiders in southern Africa. It has a neurotoxic poison, which affects both the heart and respiratory function. The bite is painful and produces symptoms within half an hour. These are alarming and include anxiety, severe chest and abdominal pains, headache, rapid changes in body temperature and a general coldness of the skin. At the site of the bite a red, inflammatory swelling forms, and often a lingering rash appears. Although these symptoms are alarming, very few deaths have been recorded in southern Africa. Antivenom is available from the South African Institute for Medical Research in Johannesburg.
COLLECTING METHODS: Hand-to-jar

Comb on fourth tarsus

The most infamous member of this vast family is the black widow spider, better known in southern Africa as the black button spider, *Latrodectus indistinctus* (previously *L. mactans*). These are black, medium-sized spiders, most having some form of orange-red marking or markings on the dorsal side of the abdomen, although this is absent in some adult females. They never have any red markings on the ventral side of the abdomen. (The American *L. mactans* has an hour-glass marking ventrally.) *L. indistinctus* is sedentary and usually found in the field; it is not common in populated areas. The black button spider is one of the more dangerous spiders in southern Africa, having a neurotoxic poison.

The brown or house button spider *L. geometricus* (see plate 60) and the Rhodesian button spider *L. rhodesiensis* are the button spiders in southern Africa that show the characteristic hour-glass pattern on the ventral side of the abdomen. Both these button spiders may vary in colour from light yellowish-brown, with geometric patterns on the dorsal side of the abdomen, to pitch black. The brown or house button spider is found in abundance in and around human habitation, especially outbuildings, garages, verandas and under window ledges. The Rhodesian button spider is found in grasslands and bush country, and also around houses, but is not very common in South Africa.

The black button spider

Theridiids are small to medium-sized spiders having a globose abdomen and long legs of which the third pair is the shortest. They are sedentary, hanging upside-down in their webs. They have comb-like setae, consisting of a row of six to 10 modified hairs, on the tarsus of the fourth leg. These setae are used to fling out the silk over the prey at capture.

The brown button spider

The three button spiders in black phase may be difficult to tell apart, especially by the amateur. However, their egg sacs differentiate them immediately. *L. indistinctus* makes a smooth, round, whitish-yellow egg sac about 10 mm in diameter, and more than one is commonly found in the web. The web of *L. geometricus* also commonly houses more than one egg sac, but these are slightly smaller and always spiky and irregular in shape. *L. rhodesiensis* makes an impressive cluster of four or five large, fluffy balls of soft outer silk; when held up to the light the smaller, more dense ball containing the eggs can be seen within each fluffy outer covering.

Dew-drop spider

Egg sacs of comb-footed spiders

Steatoda is often mistaken for a black or brown button spider. However, on close examination the spider can be seen to be brownish-black with no markings ventrally, and with a creamish-white marking on the anterior dorsal aspect of the abdomen. Males may be confused with those of *Latrodectus* but have a distinctive scutum or shield behind the pedicel on the front of the abdomen.

Theridion or false button spiders are smaller than the true button spiders (never more than 5–6 mm) and generally have a creamy brown to dark brown abdomen with irregular markings. Their legs appear to be striped. These small spiders are commonly found in houses, often in the bath or sink.

Argyrodes (dew-drop spiders) are small,

Comb-footed spider, hanging in web

often silver-coloured spiders that are klepto-parasitic, living in the webs of other spiders, especially those of *Argiope* and *Cyrtophora* (see pages 28 and 31) and *Nephila* (see page 52), where they eat discarded prey remains. The males of some *Argyrodes* have enlarged, deformed protruberances at the front of the carapace, like the Erigoninae (see page 65). In some species the abdomen is long and tail-like in appearance.

Theridiids make many different kinds of webs, from those with an irregular network of strong threads without any apparent design (commonly called cobwebs) to the so-called scaffold webs forming a three-dimensional trellis of silken threads with drop lines running from the lower mantle of the web to the ground or substrate, and often with knockdown lines of strong silk attaching the upper part of the mantle to leaves, branches or other overhead attachment points. The drop lines are designed according to whether the spider is capturing flying or crawling prey; if the former then droplets of gluey silk are deposited about halfway up the lines, if the latter then the gluey droplets are placed on the lines near to the ground. The upper knockdown lines knock flying insects onto the mantle, where capture is made.

Some of the species make a retreat with a ventral opening centred in the web, while others, like *Latrodectus*, have retreats to the side of the web. Some of the smaller species do not make webs of their own but live in and about the webs of other spiders.

Many of the theridiid species tend to be sedentary, not leaving their intricate web once this has been set up.

71

Net-Casting Spiders

FAMILY: **Deinopidae**

NET-CASTING SPIDERS

COMMON GENERA: *Deinopis, Menneus, Avellopsis*

LIFESTYLE: Free-running, plant-living
NOCTURNAL

Members of this family are stick-like spiders, and they have a remarkable and unique method of capturing prey. The net-casting spiders' most important characteristics are the modification of the abdomen where one, two or no humps are present; the eye pattern (see *Deinopis*); the very long legs; and the method of prey capture.

A. *DEINOPIS* (OGRE-FACED SPIDERS)

    ·

HABITAT: In built-up areas; in and up trees; on bushes and plants or in low base vegetation; in forests
SIZE: Medium to large. 12–30 mm. Female slightly larger than male
POISON: Harmless
COLLECTING METHODS: Beating; hand-to-jar; night collecting

Eye pattern of Deinopis *sp.*

The female ogre-faced spider is uniformly blackish-brown and covered with a coating of whitish-yellow hairs. In the male the carapace and abdomen are dark olive-brown with silver-white marginal bands. The posterior median eyes are set far forward and are greatly enlarged, hence the common name.

Deinopis captures its prey by casting a rectangular, expandable web over it. This web is made of calamistrated silk. The spider holds the four corners of the web with its first two pairs of legs, and hangs head downwards a few centimetres above the ground, supported by a scaffolding of non-sticky silk. When prey wanders beneath the waiting spider, the web is 'thrown' over it, much like the retiarius of a gladiator.

Deinopis makes its web after nightfall and awaits prey during the dark hours. During the day it may be found pressed flat against the bark of a branch or twig with the long two pairs of front legs stretched forwards and the back four legs grasping the twig firmly.

Not a common spider, it has been collected from small bushes in Natal and the Transvaal and from coastal bush and fynbos in the Cape and Natal.

B. *MENNEUS* (HUMPED-BACK SPIDERS)

     ·

HABITAT: In built-up areas; in and up trees; on bushes and plants and in low base vegetation; in, on or under grass; in forests
SIZE: Medium to large. 12–30 mm. Female slightly larger than male
POISON: Harmless
COLLECTING METHODS: Sweep-netting; beating; hand-to-jar; night collecting

The outstanding characteristic of these spiders is the presence of a large, single hump situated to one side of the abdomen of the female; in males the abdomen is long and straight. Their colour resembles the bark of the trees on which they rest during the daylight hours, generally yellowish-brown, and they are clothed in white hairs and mottled with brown markings (see plate 20). The eyes are in two rows with the anterior row slightly procurved and the posterior row slightly recurved. Under magnification and looked at from above, the front of the carapace looks not unlike that of the head of a barbel.

Eye pattern of Menneus sp.

The prey capture method of *Menneus* is similar to that of *Deinopis*, except that *Menneus* is not reliant on prey walking beneath it. *Menneus* tends to await prey on grass stems and twigs near the ground, and when prey comes within reach the spider expands its net to five or six times its size and 'hurls' itself and the web upon it, from whatever angle.

A nocturnal hunter, *Menneus* begins its web-spinning at twilight. It is found throughout southern Africa but is not common.

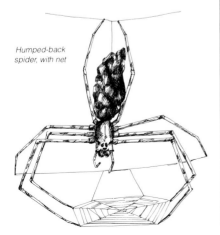

Humped-back spider, with net

C. *AVELLOPSIS* (CAMEL-BACK SPIDERS)

 ·

HABITAT: On bushes and plants or in low base vegetation
SIZE: Medium to large. 6–15 mm. Female slightly larger than male
POISON: Harmless
COLLECTING METHODS: Sweep-netting; beating; hand-to-jar

The only known species belonging to this genus, *A. capensis*, is recorded from the Cape Province. They are smaller than their cousins, but closely resemble *Menneus*, having a similar colour and eye pattern. The carapace is distinctive in being wider over the thoracic area and the abdomen presents with two humps in both males and females.

Nothing is known about the behaviour of these spiders.

Kleptoparasites

FAMILY: **Mimetidae**
CANNIBAL SPIDERS
COMMON GENERA: *Ero, Mimetus*

 ·  ·

LIFESTYLE: Free-running, plant-living
HABITAT: In other spiders' webs
SIZE: Small to medium. 4-10 mm
NOCTURNAL
POISON: Harmless
COLLECTING METHODS: Sweep-netting; beating; hand-to-jar; night collecting

Both genera of this family are easily identified by the unique and characteristic spinations on the two long front legs (*Ero* has spines on

Spines

the second leg as well), and by their distinctively marked and globose abdomen. They usually hunt alone in the webs of other species of spiders, and are unique in that they prey exclusively on other spiders.

Placed by some authors with the hunters, the mimetid is, however, sluggish when compared to the free runners. It climbs surreptitiously onto the webs of other spiders, mainly theridiids (see page 69) and orb weavers such as *Araneus*, the hairy field spider (see page 29). During the day it usually remains motionless, and becomes active at dusk and dawn – as Lawrence (1981) puts it, 'the most fitting hours for the assassin and terrorist'. As night falls it begins to pluck at and vibrate its host's web, and when the inhabitant comes to investigate the mimetid stretches its armed forelegs up, forwards and over the host, pulling it down. Quickly it bites into the femur of the first leg of its prey and, according to Lawrence, 'death is almost instantaneous'. The empty shell of the dead spider is left hanging in its own snare.

Cannibal spider

FAMILY: **Mysmenidae**

MIDGET KLEPTOPARASITE SPIDERS

COMMON GENUS: *Isela*

 · ·

LIFESTYLE: Free-running, plant-living
HABITAT: In other spiders' webs
SIZE: Tiny to very small. 0,5-2 mm

DIURNAL / NOCTURNAL
POISON: Harmless
COLLECTING METHODS: Hand-to-jar; pooter

This family is formed by a group of spiders recently removed from the family Symphytognathidae. They are tiny, unsclerotized spiders with a spherical abdomen, eight eyes and three tarsal claws. Kleptoparasites, they have been found living on the sheet webs of the diplurid spider *Allothele* (see page 116), where they feed on abandoned prey.

Free-Living Ground Spiders

FAMILY: **Anyphaenidae**

SEASHORE SPIDERS

COMMON GENUS: *Amaurobioides*

 ·

LIFESTYLE: Free-running, ground-living
HABITAT: On the seashore
SIZE: Medium-large to large. 13–17 mm. Female larger than male
DIURNAL / NOCTURNAL
POISON: Harmless
COLLECTING METHOD: Hand-to-jar

Seashore spider

Dark reddish-brown to black spiders, sea-shore spiders have robust legs covered with fine hairs known as hydrofuge setae. The legs are not armed with spines, and have two claws. The eyes are situated on a low protuberance in a compact group, and are encircled with black. The chelicerae are stout, almost bulbous, and the fangs are strong. The abdomen has a distinctive black-brown chevron pattern on the dorsal aspect (see plate 21).

The anyphaenids live along the coast of the eastern and western Cape, restricted to beaches where rocky faces are present. They live within the seaspray range known as the splash zone, between the high-water neap and high-water spring tide delimitations. Unlike the long-jawed intertidal spiders (see page 79), they become submerged only during the spring tides.

In areas with strong wave action, they make a web-lined nest under a limpet shell or in an empty barnacle, closing it completely during the spring tide. The lining is made of strong silk and is watertight, and enough oxygen is sealed in for prolonged immersion. In areas with weak wave action, the spiders do not build nests but with the help of their hydrofuge setae trap enough air around the body to supply them with oxygen during their period of submersion.

When not submerged, seashore spiders roam around the rocks in search of prey which is comprised mainly of various intertidal arthropods.

These spiders are found only in the southern hemisphere, and only one species, *A. africanus*, is recorded from the region.

FAMILY: **Ammoxenidae**

SAND-DIVERS

COMMON GENUS: *Ammoxenus*

 ·   ·

LIFESTYLE: Free-running, ground-living
HABITAT: On or under sand; on open ground; in semi-arid desert; in association with insects
SIZE: Small to medium. 3–7 mm
DIURNAL
POISON: Harmless
COLLECTING METHODS: Hand-to-jar; pitfall trap

Sand-diver

Extremely fast and agile, ammoxenids are not often seen. They are adapted to life in sandy soils, especially those mounds of fine sandy grains made by termites. Not unlike the zodariids (see page 61) in appearance, they are, however, covered with dense, recumbent, plumose hairs, giving them a greasy appearance. The abdomen is oval in shape and in most species there are cream-coloured markings down the sides and middle on the dorsal aspect (see plate 22). The legs are long and covered with hairs; the tarsi, especially, are very long and flexible and curl up in preserved specimens. The eyes are arranged in a compact group on a small protuberance on the front of the carapace. The chelicerae are modified for burrowing.

These spiders are usually found around the nests of termites, on which they prey. When foraging, they travel rapidly over the ground, and even more rapidly dive into the sand head-first if disturbed or threatened. During their non-active periods you may find them concealed in the soil humps of the termites, where they cover themselves with a thin layer of slightly sticky silk.

The egg sac, which resembles a cup without a handle, is concealed in the soil hump.

Ammoxenids are found throughout southern Africa but their association with termites affects their distribution from region to region.

FAMILY: **Anapidae**
DWARF RING-SHIELD SPIDERS

COMMON GENUS: *Crozetulus* (incorporates those species previously listed under *Speleoderces*)

 ·   ·

LIFESTYLE: Sedentary, web-bound
HABITAT: In forests; in caves
SIZE: Tiny. 1-1,3 mm
DIURNAL / NOCTURNAL
POISON: Harmless
COLLECTING METHODS; Hand-to-jar; tullgren funnel; sifting; pooter

The abdomen of the tiny anapids is usually covered with two or three scuta. In the female a large scutum is present dorsally on the abdomen, while the ventral scutum surrounds the pedicel.

Crozetulus has a raised carapace. The patella of the first leg in the male spider is very long and has two small apophyses. The booklungs are replaced by tracheae. The anterior median eyes are usually reduced in size or are absent. In the female the palp is also either reduced in size or is absent and the legs are spineless.

Very little is known about the anapids except that they are collected mainly from forest litter and caves. Only one species, *C. scutatus*, is known to occur in southern Africa, and it was collected from the Wynberg caves on Table Mountain.

Anapids were previously placed in the family Leptonetidae.

FAMILY: **Archaeidae**
LONG-NECK SPIDERS

COMMON GENUS: *Afrarchaea* (African long-neck spiders)

LIFESTYLE: Free-running, ground-living
HABITAT: In scrapes or free-running, under stones; on open ground; in and under leaf litter and rotting logs; in forests
SIZE: Small. 2,5-3,5 mm
DIURNAL / NOCTURNAL
POISON: Harmless
COLLECTING METHODS: Hand-to-jar; pitfall trap; tullgren funnel; sifting; rock turning

Long-neck spider

The archaeids are rare, small and strange-looking spiders. They are easily recognized under magnification by the cephalic region of the carapace, which is raised high above the thoracic region, hence the common name.

The surface of the reddish-brown carapace is covered with small, flattened protuberances, each with a short, thick, white seta. The anterior median eyes are large and dark while the others are smaller and paler in colour. The chelicerae are much enlarged, long and slender, with the fangs short and well curved. The legs are also reddish-brown and are long and slender, with the first pair the longest and the third pair the shortest. The abdomen is globular, with patches of chitinous tissue, and is covered overall with glaborous setae. The male has a scute dorsally on the anterior part of the abdomen.

Slow-moving hunters, long-neck spiders do not construct a snare or retreat. They are cryptozoic and live in damp places such as in leaf litter and under stones, and have been observed feeding on other spiders. Although they have a reasonably wide distribution in forest areas they are seldom collected, even when specifically searched for.

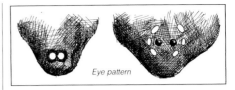

Eye pattern

FAMILY: Caponiidae
LUNGLESS ORANGE SPIDERS

COMMON GENERA: *Caponia* (eight-eyed orange spiders), *Diplogena* (two-eyed orange spiders)

LIFESTYLE: Free-running, ground-living
HABITAT: In webbing, scrapes or free-running, under stones; on open ground; in semi-arid desert
SIZE: Medium to medium-large. 6–15 mm. Female slightly larger than male
NOCTURNAL
POISON: Harmless
COLLECTING METHODS: Hand-to-jar; pitfall trap; rock turning

Lungless orange spider

The caponiids are easily recognized by the deep yellow to orange colour of the legs and carapace. They have no booklungs and breathe through two pairs of trachea situated anteriorly on the abdomen. The number of eyes varies from two (in *Diplogena*) to eight (in *Caponia*). The carapace is shield-like, like that of the palpimanids (see page 103), but the first leg is not as thick and robust. The abdomen, oval in shape, is pale yellow to pale grey, and clothed with fine black hairs. The legs have no true spines, but the tarsi have three claws.

Lungless spiders do not build webs but are swift runners and pursue their prey over the ground, overpowering it once they catch it with their strong chelicerae and robust legs. They hide under stones, where a small, oval retreat is made of transparent silk. *Diplogena* is rare; only one species, *D. capensis*, is found in the drier parts of the Cape Province and Namibia. Various species of *Caponia* are found in most parts of southern Africa.

FAMILY: Clubionidae
SAC SPIDERS

COMMON GENERA: *Clubiona* (leaf-curling sac spiders), *Cheiracanthium* (long-legged sac spiders), *Castianeira, Copa, Graptartia*

LIFESTYLE: Free-running, ground-living; free-running, plant-living
HABITAT: In built-up areas; on or under bark; in webbing, scrapes or free-running, under stones; on bushes and plants or in low base vegetation; on flowers or leaves; in and under leaf litter and rotting logs; in forests
SIZE: Small to medium-large. 4–16 mm
NOCTURNAL
POISON: Venomous. The poison is cytotoxic in action; within 24 hours the site becomes inflamed

and swollen, and it ulcerates after a few days. The ulcerative wound is very slow in healing and often becomes subject to secondary infection. Accompanying fever and malaise may be present, often with severe headache.
COLLECTING METHODS: Sweep-netting; beating; hand-to-jar; pitfall trap

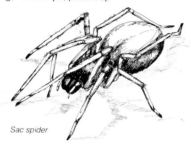

Sac spider

The clubionids are two-clawed spiders that resemble the gnaphosids (see page 96) in general appearance, but lack the gnaphosids' characteristic spinnerets. Their own special characteristic is the 'black face' appearance and, in *Clubiona* and *Cheiracanthium*, the compact body coloured in various shades of cream, light brown and yellow.

Clubionids have long legs, with the scopulae on the tarsi very dark brown or black. The chelicerae are long and rather stout, and are black. Some species have chevron markings on the abdomen. The eyes are small, almost the same size, and situated in two transverse rows. *Clubiona* usually has the fourth leg the longest, while *Cheiracanthium* has the first leg the longest.

The ground-living clubionids include a group of medium-sized, dark-coloured spiders with slender legs and hard, often granular, integument. Some species (such as

Sac spider face

Castianeira and *Copa*) mimic ants in general appearance and behaviour, while some (*Graptartia*) mimic wasps.

Sac spiders are free-roaming, aggressive hunters. They catch their prey with great speed and agility, leaping on it and grabbing it with outstretched front legs.

Most members of this family construct tubular or flat sacs of dense white silk, either open at the ends or closed, to use as a retreat. *Clubiona* makes a sac in rolled-up leaves, in folded blades of grass or under loose bark. *Cheiracanthium*, which is often found inside houses, makes a flattened, disc-shaped sac in the folds of curtains, behind and under objects and in cupboards. The sacs are papery and shiny in appearance, and very tough. The egg sac is similar but smaller.

Being wanderers at night, these spiders often move over sleeping humans and, being aggressive, will bite at the slightest provocation. Bites (which are painless) are most often recorded on the face and neck or hands, and are characterized by two bite marks approximately 6 mm apart. *Cheiracanthium lawrencei* is the species known to inflict bites with significant consequences (see plate 54).

The ground-dwelling spiders are most often found in leaf litter and among stones in open grassland.

FAMILY: **Ctenidae**

WANDERING SPIDERS

COMMON GENUS: *Ctenus*

 ·

LIFESTYLE: Free-running, ground-living
HABITAT: In built-up areas; in webbing, scrapes or free-running, under stones; on rocks or in crevices of rocks; in and under leaf litter and rotting logs; in forests
SIZE: Large to very large. 20–35 mm

NOCTURNAL
POISON: Mildly venomous. It has been found that the bite of some South American species has a toxic effect on man. The poison appears to be neurotoxic, affecting the heart and respiratory function. Being night wanderers, these spiders may pose a threat by getting into shoes and sleeping bags on the ground. Ctenids should be handled with care.
COLLECTING METHODS: Hand-to-jar; night collecting; pitfall trap; rock turning

Wandering spider in threatening pose

Wandering spider

In general, the smaller ctenid spiders resemble the wolf spiders (see page 99), and the larger ctenids resemble the large wandering crab spiders (see page 97). They are marked with cryptic colouring. They have the typical long legs of the heteropodids, but they do not pull these back when at rest as the heteropodids do. The legs are strong, with stout spines, and the tarsi have two claws and scopulae. The eyes are in three rows, with the anterior median eyes making up the first row and the middle row being made up of the posterior median and anterior lateral eyes; the anterior lateral eyes are small and are situated close to the larger posterior median eyes and as such may be overlooked. The posterior laterals, making up the third row, are slightly smaller and lie towards the sides of the head.

Ctenid spiders are wandering hunters and do not make webs. They often hold the front pair of legs high off the ground as they move

rapidly over the undergrowth in search of prey. They are aggressive and will attack at the slightest provocation; when threatened the spider 'sits back', raising the first two pairs of legs high above the head, almost perpendicular to the ground, and pushes the chelicerae forward.

They are found in the leaves of forest humus and in the cracks of rock formations, and the smaller species are common in and about the humus of compost heaps in the back garden. Here they may be passed off as 'just another wolf spider'!

FAMILY: Desidae

LONG-JAWED INTERTIDAL SPIDERS

COMMON GENUS: *Desis*

 · ·

LIFESTYLE: Free-running, ground-living
HABITAT: On the seashore
SIZE: Large. 18–20 mm (chelicerae included)
DIURNAL / NOCTURNAL
POISON: Harmless
COLLECTING METHOD: Hand-to-jar

These formidable-looking spiders with their uniform greyish-brown body and brown cephalothorax grow to up to 20 mm in length. They have greatly enlarged chelicerae and fangs which project forwards — these alone make up one third of the spider's total length (see plate 23). The legs are well developed and 'stubby', designed for gripping firmly

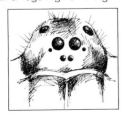

Ctenid eye pattern

onto rocks, as these spiders are prone to rigorous wave action, living as they do at the lower levels of the flooding area. *Desis* is slightly larger than the other intertidal spider, *Amaurobioides* (see page 74), and as with *Amaurobioides* it has no special aquatic adaptations to its chosen habitat.

Desis lives entirely along rocky shores, favouring the area between the normal low- and high-water marks, so is subjected to frequent periods of flooding (it is submerged every day) and more rigorous wave action. It builds its retreat in a place that offers good protection, such as a deserted mollusc shell or a crack in a rock. As such sites are often in short supply, the spiders vie with one another for the use of them, smaller spiders often being evicted by larger specimens. The retreat is lined with waterproof webbing, but if this does become flooded, the air adhering to the waxy hairs of the spider will supply it with oxygen until the next low tide.

When its habitat is not flooded, *Desis* emerges to forage. It roams in search of its intertidal arthropod prey which, because of the niche occupied by *Desis*, differs from that of *Amaurobioides*. There is some overlapping, however, and if the spiders meet and confront each other, *Desis* is usually the victor.

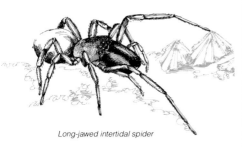

Long-jawed intertidal spider

FAMILY: **Drymusidae**

SIX-EYED LEAF LITTER SPIDERS

COMMON GENUS: *Drymusa*

 ·   ·

LIFESTYLE: Free-running, ground living
HABITAT: In and under leaf litter and rotting logs; in forests
SIZE: Small. 4,5 mm
DIURNAL / NOCTURNAL
POISON: Harmless
COLLECTING METHODS: Hand-to-jar; pitfall trap; tullgren funnel; sifting; pooter

Six-eyed leaf litter spider

Previously placed under the family Syctodidae, these small, blackish-brown spiders have long, slender legs like *Syctodes* (see page 106), but may be distinguished from them by the depressed carapace carrying a dark 'V'-shaped pattern, and by having a much wider clypeus. The six eyes are arranged in three diads and the chelicerae are fused at the base. Simple genitalia are evident and a colulus is easily seen, especially in the females.

A feature distinguishing them from another one-time Syctodidae family member, *Loxosceles* (now incorporated in the family Loxoscelidae, see page 98), is that they have three claws, as opposed to two in *Loxosceles*. Of their slender legs, the third pair is noticeably the longest.

Little is known about their behaviour, but from observations it is thought that the webbing is not used for prey capture; it seems reasonable to assume therefore that they follow the behaviour patterns of their ex family members, that is hunting freely for prey among leaf litter.

Drymusa has been collected in lowland rain forests, often having been found in or near loose webs under logs and fallen trees.

38 Thomisidae Thomisus *sp. Small crab-spider (p. 110). Ambushers par exellence, some crab spiders are known to take on the colour of the plant on which they are resting.*

39 Thomisidae Thomisus *sp. Small crab-spider (p. 110). This yellow specimen, disguised on a yellow flower, has caught a bee, which she has immobilized with her venom, harmless to man but deadly to prey.*

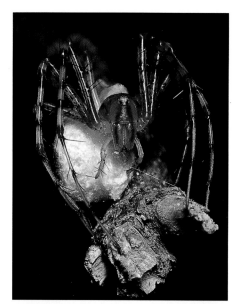
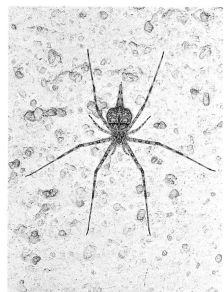

42 Thomisidae Runcinia *sp. Small crab-spider (p. 110). Awaiting passing prey, resting on a blade of grass with legs outstretched and body flattened, the spider becomes almost invisible.*

40 (far left) Oxyopidae Peucetia sp. Green lynx spider (p. 111). Foliage dwellers, lynx spiders may be seen leaping from leaf to leaf either in pursuit of prey or to escape a predator.

41 (left) Hersiliidae Hersilia sp. Long- spinnered bark spider (p. 112). This spider, photographed on a white background, becomes almost invisible on the bark of a tree.

43 (right) Trochanteriidae Platyoides sp. Scorpion spider (p. 112). The second joint of the legs, especially that of the fourth pair, is elongated and allows the spider to fold its legs up and over the body.

44 Ctenizidae Stasimopus sp. Trapdoor spider (p. 115). This smallish mygalomorph is able to dig a burrow and construct a substantial, tightly fitting, hinged trapdoor with which to seal it.

45 (left) Ctenizidae Stasimopus sp. Trapdoor spider (p. 115). Lined with silk, the trapdoor fits snugly. The spider keeps it tightly closed by holding it with the spines on its front legs.

46 (below) Idiopidae Goryrella sp. Front-eyed trapdoor spider (p. 117). Although remarkably similar in appearance to the trapdoor spider, this spider can be distinguished by the two eyes set forward and the remaining six set back on a low tubercle.

47 (right) Theraphosidae Ceratogyrus bechuanicus. Horned baboon spider (p. 120). A captive spider, drinking from a tub. Note the horn on the carapace.

48 (bottom right) Theraphosidae Pterinochilus sp. Golden-brown baboon spider (p. 121). These huge spiders rival the South American tarantulas in size, especially when kept in captivity. Note the tarsal tufts.

49 Theraphosidae Harpactira *sp. Common baboon spider (p. 121). Perhaps the least common, despite its name, this spider lives in an open-ended burrow.*

50 Theraphosidae Harpactirella lightfooti. *Small baboon spider (p. 121). Smaller than the other three genera, this spider is the only mygalomorph in southern Africa that is venomous to man.*

86

51 Theraphosidae Pterinochilus *sp. Golden-brown baboon spider (p. 121). When provoked, these spiders rear up in a threatening pose. They have paraxial fangs and strike downwards.*

52 A male mygalomorph spider collected at Hekpoort in the Transvaal. Although photographed, it escaped before it could be identified; a search is on for another specimen.

53 *Spiders grow by shedding their skin. Here, the carapace has split, the old 'foxy-red' skin can be seen underneath, and the 'new' spider is pulling itself up and out.*

54 *Clubionidae* Cheiracanthium lawrencei. *Sac spider (p. 78). This spider is responsible for 90 per cent of spider bites in southern Africa. The bite is painless and the venom cytotoxic.*

55 The 'sac' of a clubionid spider, built in a typical site between the folds of curtains.

56 Loxoscelidae Loxosceles sp. Violin spider (p. 99), showing typical carapace pattern.

57 Sicariidae Sicarius hahnii. Six-eyed desert crab spider (p. 108). This spider has a virulent cytotoxic poison; it is considered to be one of the most venomous spiders in the world.

58 *Loxoscelidae* Loxcosceles spiniceps. *Violin spider (p. 99). The cytotoxic poison of this spider causes an ulcerating wound.*

59 *Theridiidae* Latrodectus indistinctus. *Black widow (p. 70). The virulent neurotoxic poison of this spider affects the heart and respiratory function in man.*

60 Theridiidae Latrodectus geometricus. *Brown widow (p. 70). The common widow spider found in the home, its poison is said to be a quarter the strength of that of the black widow.*

61 Tarantulidae. Tailless whip scorpion. This quick-moving, vicious-looking arachnid is in fact completely harmless. It is found on rocks and in cracks of rocks.

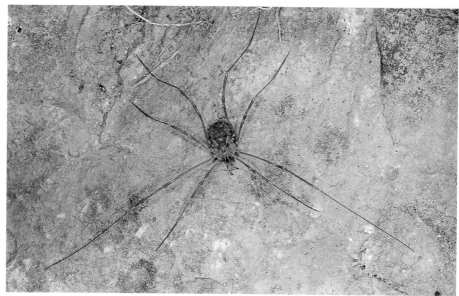

62 *Phalangiidae Harvestman. Small, extremely long-legged arachnids that are totally harmless. Most often found in leaf litter.*

63 *Solifugae. Roman spider. This harmless arachnid has no fangs, poison glands or silk apparatus, and it digests food inside rather than outside its body.*

64 Solifugae. Roman spider. Another genus of these amazing arachnids. Some authors have named them 'Sun Spiders'.

65 Scorpionidae Opistophthalmus latimanus. *Granulated burrowing scorpion. Large pincers and a thin tail indicate that the sting is not highly venomous, although very painful.*

66 (left) *Scorpionidae* Opistophthalmus glabrifrons. *Shiny burrowing scorpion. Once again, large pincers and a thin tail indicate that it is not a highly venomous scorpion.*

67 (below) *Ischnuridae* Hadogenes *sp. Rock scorpion. These large, mildly venomous scorpions have a dorsoventrally flattened abdomen and a very long tail.*

68 (right) Buthidae Parabuthus capensis. *Cape thick-tail scorpion. The small pincers and thick tail indicate that this species is highly venomous for its size.*

69 (bottom right) Buthidae Parabuthus transvaalicus. *Black hairy thick-tail scorpion. This large, aggressive scorpion is able to spray its poison up into the eyes. It is the most venomous scorpion in southern Africa.*

FAMILY: Dysderidae

GIANT-FANGED SIX-EYED SPIDERS

COMMON GENUS: *Dysdera*

LIFESTYLE: Free-running, ground-living
HABITAT: In webbing, scrapes or free-running, under stones; on open ground
SIZE: Medium to medium-large. 8–15 mm. Female slightly larger than male
NOCTURNAL
POISON: Harmless
COLLECTING METHODS: Hand-to-jar; night collecting; pitfall trap; rock turning

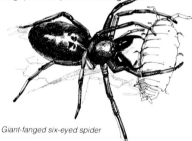

Giant-fanged six-eyed spider

Dysdera is a six-eyed spider with a bright reddish-brown, ovate carapace and a pale cream abdomen (see plate 24). The robust legs, which bear spines, are red, and there are two tarsal claws with dense claw tufts. The chelicerae are large and porrect and armed with long fangs. The six light-coloured eyes are arranged in a compact group close to the front of the carapace.

Dysderids do not build snares. They are free-running, solitary spiders, living under stones and other rubble, where they make a flattened oval retreat of tough silk. In the heat of the day they remain hidden, emerging at night to hunt. The exceptionally large chelicerae and fangs allow the spider to catch and eat woodlice, not taken by most other spiders.

Specimens have been found in the Cape.

FAMILY: Gnaphosidae

MOUSE SPIDERS

COMMON GENERA: *Drassodes, Asemesthes, Callilepis, Setaphis, Zelotes, Micaria, Prodidomus*

LIFESTYLE: Free-running, ground-living
HABITAT: In built-up areas; on or under bark; in webbing, scrapes or free-running, under stones; in and under leaf litter and rotting logs
SIZE: Medium-large to large. 10–20 mm
NOCTURNAL
POISON: Harmless
COLLECTING METHODS: Hand-to-jar; night collecting; pitfall trap; rock turning

Dull-coloured spiders, ranging from khaki yellow to dark brown or black, some genera have markings on the abdomen, which is clothed with fine hairs, hence the common name. Sometimes the hairs may glisten with a metallic brightness (see plate 25).

Gnaphosids form a large family of more than 200 species, some having an ovate carapace while others have a narrow and oblong carapace. The eyes are in two rows, commonly both procurved, with the posterior median eyes in some species oval and set at an angle. The chelicerae of these spiders are robust, but more slender than those of the Clubionidae (see page 77); they are often boldly dark brown, with black fangs curving inwards and overlapping. (This feature is most obvious in the subfamily Prodidominae.)

Mouse spider

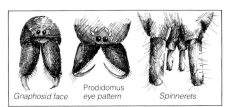

Gnaphosid face | Prodidomus eye pattern | Spinnerets

Gnaphosids tend to have a long, slightly flattened abdomen and characteristic spinnerets. These are cylindrical and are markedly parallel to and separate from each other.

Mouse spiders build small, irregular nests, mainly under stones, made of strong, sheet-like webbing. Some of these nests may have a tube-like retreat at one end. Most species are nocturnal wanderers, searching out prey and overcoming it with speed and force. The prey is then enswathed with bands of silk. Lawrence (1964) states that as gnaphosids have poor eyesight '... prey is perceived by tactile or chemotactic stimuli'.

FAMILY: **Heteropodidae**
LARGE WANDERING CRAB SPIDERS

COMMON GENERA: *Palystes* (rain spiders), *Olios* (rock-rain spiders), *Leucorchestris* (white ladies), *Carparachne* (wheeling spiders), *Pseudomicrommata* (green grass spiders), *Palystella, Panaretella*

LIFESTYLE: Free-running, ground-living; free-running, plant-living
HABITAT: In built-up areas; in and up trees; on or under bark; in webbing, scrapes or free-running, under stones; on rocks or in crevices of rocks; on bushes and plants or in low base vegetation; in, on or under grass; in and under leaf litter and rotting logs; in semi-arid desert
SIZE: *Palystes* and *Olios* large to very large, 25–35 mm. *Leucochestris, Carparachne* and *Palystella* large, 15–30 mm. *Pseudomicrommata* and *Panaretella* medium-large to large, 10–20 mm
DIURNAL / NOCTURNAL
POISON: Harmless
COLLECTING METHODS: Sweep-netting; hand-to-jar; night collecting; pitfall trap; rock turning

Palystes *eye pattern*

The giant wandering crab spiders are just that — they are large, nocturnal, free-wandering hunters that do not construct webs for prey capture. Most genera are covered with a fine pile of light, straw-grey to dark brown hairs. The carapace is broader than it is long. The clypeus of *Palystes* shows a white band, rather like a white moustache, and the eye pattern of the family is in two rows, with the anterior laterals often the largest. They have long, robust legs, turned outwards in crab-like fashion. At rest or in defence all the legs are characteristically drawn backwards and held close to the body, but in aggression the front legs or the first two pairs of legs are raised high over the head.

Palystes, the most commonly seen genus, tends to be a dark brown spider and has often

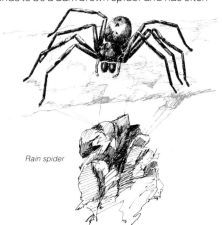

Rain spider

97

been mistaken for one of the baboon spiders (see page 120). Its abdomen may be unmarked or have a blackish, shield-shaped chevron pattern (clearly seen in gravid females). The underside of the legs show bands of yellow to darkish orange at the leg joints (see plate 26). A brush of red scopulae on the chelicerae is displayed as a deterrent as the spider raises its legs and pushes the chelicerae forwards to frighten the aggressor.

Olios is a smaller spider and is usually a pearly cream colour, with black chelicerae and straw-brown legs.

Leucorchestris and *Carparachne*, the large desert spiders, are known as the 'dancing white ladies' because of their coloration and strange, prancing behaviour when threatened. *Leucorchestris* is the real 'white lady', as her latin name implies; *Carparachne* escapes danger by cartwheeling. Very pale off-white, these two genera are very similar in looks to the larger *Palystes*, except that the legs are armed with spines.

Pseudomicrommata, a smaller member of the family, lives in the grasslands and, apart from by its size, is distinguished from the other members of the family by having well-defined red or reddish-brown bands down the body. Some species may be green in colour.

The heteropodids are nocturnal in the wild, coming out at night to hunt. In built-up areas they may be active during the day due to the comings and goings of humans. *Palystes* is most often seen indoors on walls, attracted by the insects brought in by the light. Resting with its long legs outstretched, it will move away with great speed if disturbed. Its behaviour has given rise to a number of common names such as 'rain spider' (as it often comes indoors before the rain, when insects are prevalent), 'wall spider' (because of its ambushing position on the wall), and 'lizard-eating spider' (as it is known to feed on the small wall gecko *Lygodactylus*). The females of *Palystes* make a large bag of papery white silk and leaves (see plate 27). These 'bags of leaves' are found in hedges or shrubs and in low base vegetation, and are attached to surrounding branches and leaves by strong strands of silk.

White lady

The female crouches behind or below the nest, protecting her brood.

Olios makes a retreat of papery white silk under rocks. This oval nest is firmly attached to the substrate and is difficult to move. Its entrance may be covered with bits of leaves. If it is pulled open, the spider darts out and runs around to the opposite side of the rock. (This behaviour often leads to the demise of the spider as the collector may drop the rock in fright, crushing the spider.)

The dancing white ladies are found only in the dune areas of the Namib Desert. *Carparachne* digs a sloping burrow into the slip-face of the dune, lining it with blobs of sand and sticky webbing. *Leucorchestris* makes its burrow on the flat desert surface, a deep narrow tube into which the spider just manages to squeeze. When threatened, *Carparachne*, the smaller of the two, folds in its legs and 'throws' itself down the side of the dune, cartwheeling at great speed. On reaching the bottom it rapidly burrows into the sand and disappears from view. *Leucorchestris's* prancing behaviour and its standing on 'tip-toe' is characteristic (see plate 28).

Pseudomicrommata makes a large nest in *Eragrostis* grass, and is confined to areas where this grass is found. *Palystella* is found in the dry areas of the northern Cape, the Kalahari and Namibia, while the smaller *Panaretella* occurs in coastal forests.

FAMILY: Loxoscelidae
VIOLIN SPIDERS

COMMON GENUS: *Loxosceles*

 ·

LIFESTYLE: Free-running, ground-living
HABITAT: In built-up areas; on or under bark; in webbing, scrapes or free-running, under stones; in and under leaf litter and rotting logs; in forests; in disused holes; in caves
SIZE: Medium-large. 8–15 mm (leg span up to 40 mm). Female slightly larger than male
NOCTURNAL
POISON: Venomous. The cytotoxic poison causes a nasty ulcerating wound, often involving severe secondary infection. The resulting tissue damage leaves disfiguring scars which may require plastic surgery.
COLLECTING METHODS: Hand-to-jar; night collecting; pitfall trap; sifting

The violin spiders are often mistaken for members of the family Pholcidae (see page 69). They have six eyes arranged in three well-separated pairs. Their colour varies from brick-brown to rich red-brown, with darker markings on the abdomen. They have a characteristic dark brown to black violin-shaped marking on the carapace, which gives them their common name (see plates 56 and 58). The carapace is relatively flat, with the abdomen oval-shaped and the legs long and slender. A long, obvious colulus is present.

Carapace pattern

Loxosceles is never web-bound. It roams freely at night in search of prey; it is this behaviour that readily distinguishes it from the pholcids, which are web-bound. The natural habitat of the savanna species is under rocks and logs, beneath the bark of fallen trees, in old termite nests, among rubble and in deserted human habitations. Three species are cave dwellers. One of the spelaean

species, *L. parrami*, has been artificially introduced into human habitation on the Witwatersrand and is found in the cracks and crevices of walls, behind picture frames and in dark corners of cupboards and drawers.

Violin spider

FAMILY: Lycosidae
WOLF SPIDERS

COMMON GENERA: *Evippa, Evippoma, Hippasa* (funnel-web wolf spiders), *Lycosa, Geolycosa* (trapdoor wolf spiders), *Pardosa* (sand wolf spiders), *Zenonina*

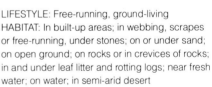

LIFESTYLE: Free-running, ground-living
HABITAT: In built-up areas; in webbing, scrapes or free-running, under stones; on or under sand; on open ground; on rocks or in crevices of rocks; in and under leaf litter and rotting logs; near fresh water; on water; in semi-arid desert
SIZE: Medium to large. 6–30 mm
DIURNAL / NOCTURNAL
POISON: Harmless
COLLECTING METHODS: Hand-to-jar; night collecting; pitfall trap; digging; rock turning

Wolf spider

'Lycosa' is the Greek word for wolf, and just like their namesake these spiders are vagabonds which lie in wait to run down their prey. They are easily recognized by their characteristic eye pattern. The eyes are arranged in three rows. The anterior four eyes are very small and either straight or curved gently downwards; the two larger posterior medians are situated on the vertical front of the carapace; and the two smaller posterior lateral eyes are above and to the sides of the head, making up the third row.

Wolf spider, with egg sac

Lycosid face

Most southern African species are pale creamy brown to grey, with darker markings on the carapace and abdomen (see plate 29). The abdomen is oval and has brown, orange, grey and black chevron patterns, and although at first glance they appear rather drab, on closer examination some species are quite beautiful. In some species of *Lycosa*, which are pale cream in colour, the chevrons become bold and attractive and their chelicerae show a pillarbox red when the spider is threatened. The ventral aspect of the abdomen is sometimes jet-black, with distinctive white markings. *Hippasa* is a fairly large, olive-brown to black spider, with two rows of white spots on the abdomen and long, superior spinnerets rather like those of the grass funnel-web spiders (see page 116). *Pardosa* and *Evippa* are the smaller members of the family and are creamy brown to black. Often the legs of the lycosids have a typically banded appearance.

The habit of the female of carrying the egg sac attached to her spinnerets enables one to recognize the family even from a distance.

Free-roaming hunters, wolf spiders are active by both day and night, in and out of doors. They can be collected with ease at night

because their eyes reflect bright green under torch light and they remain motionless as one approaches. The smaller wolf spiders, mainly *Pardosa* (which grow to 10 mm), roam freely among stones and low vegetation and are often seen on lawns, especially after these have been newly mown. Some species of *Pardosa* are semi-aquatic and live near or on the water. *Evippa* have similar habits to *Pardosa*, but are characteristic of desert and semi-arid regions.

The larger representatives, mainly *Lycosa*, appear to be quite dozy, but if disturbed will run away at speed, in leaps and jumps, or rear up, front legs raised in defence. *Geolycosa* lives in burrows, like the trapdoor spiders (see page 115 and plate 30).

Hippasa is the exception to the rule in this family in being sedentary, with behaviour similar to that of the agelenids (see page 62). They build a typical funnel-shaped web with a platform, like those of the agelenids. (An 'agelenid' in a funnel web with an egg sac attached to the spinnerets must therefore be a lycosid, genus *Hippasa*!)

After laying and securing her eggs in a sac, the female lycosid attaches this 'ball' to her spinnerets, and it remains there until the young emerge. Often she can be seen traversing rough and stony terrain, with the egg sac seemingly being battered and bruised. However, this rough treatment does not appear to harm it. When the spiderlings emerge from the egg sac after having completed their first moult, they climb onto their mother's abdomen and are carried about by her for several days. Should they fall off they simply walk up a leg and back onto the abdomen again, or are lost forever, as the mother will not knowingly come back and look for them.

FAMILY: **Miturgidae**

FOREST FLOOR AND CAVE SPIDERS

LIFESTYLE: Free-running, ground-living
HABITAT: In and under leaf litter and rotting logs;
in forests; in caves
SIZE: Medium to medium-large. 6–15 mm
DIURNAL / NOCTURNAL
POISON: Harmless
COLLECTING METHODS: Hand-to-jar; pitfall trap;
tullgren funnel; sifting

SUBFAMILY: **Miturginae**

COMMON GENUS: *Syspira*

SUBFAMILY: **Machadoninae**

COMMON GENERA: *Machadonia* (incorporates
African species previously listed under
Campostichomma), *Phanotea*

Forest floor spider

This family includes both spiders with two and
those with three tarsal claws, as well as those
with and without a cribellum. In our region only
one subfamily, Machadoninae, has been recorded. Our machadonine spiders have only
two claws and lack a cribellum.

Species listed under *Machadonia* are cryptic spiders living in the damp humus of
forests. They are short-legged, robust
spiders, superficially resembling *Lycosa* (see
page 100) and *Ctenus* (see page 78). Their
colour varies from reddish-brown to blackish-
brown, with the carapace showing bands of
colour and the abdomen varied faint markings from spots to chevrons. Five species are
known from Natal and Zululand and one from
the Cape.

Species of *Phanotea* show adaptations to
cave life. Their eyes are small in comparison
with the large size of the carapace, with the
anterior row of eyes slightly recurved and the
posterior row straight or recurved. Their maxillae are large and robust. All legs have numerous, long and strong spines and, compared
to those of other cave dwellers, are large.

Machadonia is cursorial, free-living in
forest humus and leaf litter. Like other hunters,
it runs down and overpowers prey with speed
and agility. Nothing has been written thus far
about the behaviour of the cave dwellers.

FAMILY: **Oonopidae**

DWARF SIX-EYED SPIDERS

POISON: Family as a whole is harmless
COLLECTING METHODS: sweep-netting;
beating; hand-to-jar; pitfall trap; tullgren funnel;
sifting; pooter; rock turning

A family of small spiders, generally less than
3 mm in length, with six eyes, except for those
living in termite nests, which are blind. They
are divided into two distinct subfamilies,
those having soft abdomens (Oonopinae)
and those having the abdomen covered with
a hard shield or scutum (Gamasomorphinae).
Oonopids are fairly common throughout
southern Africa.

SUBFAMILY: **Oonopinae**

DWARF SIX-EYED SPIDERS

COMMON GENERA: *Oonops*, *Orchestina*,
Calculus, *Australoonops*

LIFESTYLE: Free-running, ground-living
HABITAT: In and under leaf litter and rotting logs;
on bushes and plants or in low base vegetation;
in, on, or under grass
SIZE: Very small to small. 2–4 mm
NOCTURNAL

The abdomen of this subfamily is soft and clothed in fine, pale hairs. In general it is paler in colour than the other subfamily.

The Oonopinae make no webs and are ground-living, hunting spiders. They run over the surface, often moving about in a series of jerks. Usually found under stones, leaf litter or dry vegetation, *Oonops* is sometimes found in the nests of birds. They are nocturnal and hide during the day in small retreats.

Eye pattern of Orchestina *sp.*

SUBFAMILY: **Gamasomorphinae**
DWARF SIX-EYED ARMOURED SPIDERS

COMMON GENERA: *Gamasomorpha, Opopaea, Sulsula, Dysderina*

LIFESTYLE: Free-running, ground-living
HABITAT: In webbing, scrapes or free-running,
under stones; in and under leaf litter and rotting
logs; in semi-arid desert
SIZE: Very small to small. 2–4 mm
NOCTURNAL

These are small, armoured oonopids, with two chitinous scutes (or shields) covering the dorsal and ventral sides of the abdomen. Most species have six eyes. Some, that live in termite nests, are blind. The eyes are all light

Lateral view of dwarf six-eyed armoured spider

in colour and are arranged in a compact group. The carapace, scutes and legs are orange-yellow to yellow, and the abdomen is characteristically long and oval.

Their behaviour is similar to that of the Oonopinae.

FAMILY: **Orsolobidae**

SMALL GIANT-FANGED SIX-EYED SPIDERS

COMMON GENERA: *Afrilobus, Azanialobus*

LIFESTYLE: Free-running, ground-living
HABITAT: In and under leaf litter and rotting logs;
in forests
SIZE: Tiny to small. 1–6 mm
NOCTURNAL
POISON: Harmless
COLLECTING METHODS: Hand-to-jar; pitfall trap;
tullgren funnel; pooter; rock turning

A family of six-eyed, two-clawed spiders resembling those of the family Dysderidae (see page 96), they are identified by the presence of elevated tarsal organs that are synapomorphic for the family. *Afrilobus* is distinguished from *Azanialobus* by the abdominal markings. The former has a purplish hue over the dorsum, marked with pale chevrons, while in *Azanialobus* the abdomen is pale and uniform. All legs have spines in *Afrilobus* but in *Azanialobus* there are spines only on the first and second legs.

Collection of specimens from montane forests in Malawi and Natal suggests a free-running, hunting existence in the leaf litter and humus of the forest floor. However, some species have been collected in the non-forest biome of the Cederberg in the Cape, where they roam freely in among the low scrub bushes.

Small giant-fanged six-eyed spider

FAMILY: Palpimanidae
PALP-FOOTED SPIDERS

COMMON GENERA: *Ikuma* (incorporates southern African species previously listed under *Palpimanus*), *Diaphorocellus*, *Otiothops* (incorporates those species previously listed under *Iheringia*)

 ·   ·

LIFESTYLE: Free-running, ground-living
HABITAT: In webbing, scrapes or free-running, under stones; in or under sand; on open ground; in semi-arid desert
SIZE: Medium to medium-large. 6–15 mm
NOCTURNAL
POISON: Harmless
COLLECTING METHODS: Hand-to-jar; pitfall trap; rock turning

These spiders have a sclerotized carapace, sub-oval in outline, with the head region evenly rounded and sloping back to the thoracic region. The carapace and legs are red in colour. Characteristic of the family are the greatly enlarged and armoured front legs, especially the femur. The abdomen is ovate, with the cuticle leathery and the epigastric region sclerotized, forming a scute which encircles the pedicel. *Diaphorocellus* usually has a purplish abdomen with light spots on the dorsal aspect. The eye pattern of *Ikuma* shows the posterior median eyes round and widely separated, while in *Diaphorocellus* the two posterior median eyes are triangular and subcontiguous.

Palp-footed spiders are found throughout southern Africa. They are slow-moving hunters that may be seen holding their enlarged front legs aloft. They make a small, irregular retreat web under a stone, from which they are easily extricated.

FAMILY: Pisauridae
NURSERY-WEB AND FISHING SPIDERS

POISON: Harmless
COLLECTING METHODS: Beating; hand-to-jar; pitfall trap

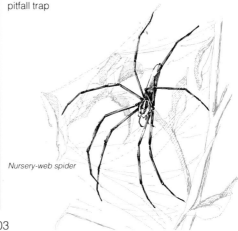

Nursery-web spider

Palp-footed spider

SUBFAMILY: **Pisaurinae**

NURSERY WEB SPIDERS

COMMON GENERA: *Euprosthenops*,
Chiasmopes (incorporates those species
previously listed under *Spencerella*), *Cispius*

   ·

LIFESTYLE: Sedentary, web-bound; free-running,
ground-living; free-running, plant-living
HABITAT: In and up trees; on open ground; on
bushes and plants or in low base vegetation; in,
on or under grass
SIZE: Large. 15–30 mm (leg span may reach
60 mm)
DIURNAL

Nursery-web spiders may be recognized by
their slender body and long legs. The elongated abdomen shows symmetrical patterns of
black on a rufous-brown to grey background.
Some species have bands of white running
down the sides of the carapace and abdomen, but these markings are more characteristic of the subfamily Thalassinae.

The long legs are armed with numerous
spines. At rest in the web, the spider most
often holds the first two pairs of legs forward
and close together. They have three claws on
each tarsus, and a colulus is present. *Euprosthenops* is the largest member of this family,
Chiasmopes and *Cispius* being smaller and
more delicate.

Euprosthenops (see plate 31) is a large,
impressive-looking spider that builds its nursery web in the middle of woody shrubs, in
trees (often *Acacia*) and in succulent plants.
The web is made of tough strands of silk
encompassing a tent-like structure, sloping
downwards at an oblique angle, often narrow-
ing into a tunnel or into the base of the plant
in which it is made. The spider hangs inverted
within the fine, tent-like webbing, and if disturbed disappears with incredible speed into
the retreat. This behaviour makes it one of the
most difficult spiders to catch.

Chiasmopes is far more delicate in body
and shape, as is its web, which is generally
made closer to the ground, in coarse grass or
small bushes. When touched, the silk of its
web breaks easily.

Cispius is active, a running hunter that pur-
sues its prey in leaps and bounds across the
substrate. Smaller by far than *Euprosthenops*,
it does show the numerous long spines on its
long, slender legs.

Females of the family make a spherical egg
sac, which they carry in the chelicerae. The
bulk of the egg sac hangs below the sternum,
making her assume a 'tip-toe' stance as she
walks to keep the eggs safely above the substrate (see plate 32). This egg sac, unlike that
of the wolf spiders (see page 99), is a single
ball enclosing the eggs. Just before the young
emerge, the female attaches the egg sac to
some leaves or twigs in low vegetation, weav-
ing around it the tent-like structure and,
around this, a secondary framework of fine
silk. Once the spiderlings have emerged they
are 'trapped' within this nursery, and remain
there for one or two instars before biting their
way out. All the while the female remains with
the nursery, guarding her young.

Nursery-web spider, with egg sac

SUBFAMILY: **Thalassinae**

FISHING SPIDERS

COMMON GENUS: *Thalassius*

 ·

LIFESTYLE: Free-running, ground-living
HABITAT: Near fresh water; on water
SIZE: Large. 15–30 mm (leg span up to 60 mm)
DIURNAL

Fishing spider, on water

LIFESTYLE: Free-running, ground-living;
free-running, plant-living
HABITAT: Found in almost every environment
SIZE: Small to medium-large. 4–16 mm
DIURNAL
POISON: Harmless
COLLECTING METHODS: Sweep-netting;
beating; hand-to-jar; pitfall trap; sifting; rock
turning; tree trap

Jumping spider

Impressive-looking spiders, the bright white borders to the body are prominent, and on the dorsal aspect of the abdomen there are most often numerous colour patterns within a chocolate-brown to black background. Distinctively, the genera of this subfamily stand with their long legs spread out, equally spaced and encircling the whole body.

Thalassius lives and hunts near pools of water with side vegetation. It moves very fast on both land and water, and can often be seen drifting on the surface of the water, being moved along by the breeze (see plate 37). Some of the larger species catch tadpoles and even small fish.

Like the other pisaurids, the female carries the egg sac around with her until the spiderlings are about to emerge and guards them until they are ready to leave the nursery.

These spiders have the best vision of all the hunting spiders, and if you get close enough you will notice the intensity of their stare. Light reflecting from the back of the eyes makes it appear as if the spider is actually following your movements, and this gives it an anthropomorphic quality (see plate 33).

Most of the genera are smaller than 5 mm, and you will need a magnifying glass to see not only the attentive look but, in the case of many of the males, the pedipalps adorned with iridescent hairs and their many-coloured

FAMILY: Salticidae

JUMPING SPIDERS

SOME COMMON GENERA: *Cyrba,
Cosmophasis, Euophrys, Habrocestum, Hasarius,
Heliophanus, Hyllus, Langona, Marengo,
Myrmarachne, Natta, Pachyballus, Phlegra,
Portia, Salticus*

Jumping spider

bodies — the common name for the male of the genus *Portia* is the dandy (see plate 35).

In most species the cephalothorax is squarish in shape and larger than the abdomen. The eye pattern is diagnostic: a pair of large anterior median eyes in the centre front of the carapace, with the anterior lateral eyes raised and to the side. The posterior eyes are set above and to the sides of the head region of the carapace. (Salticids are free-roaming hunters that 'jump' on their prey. For this they require the stereoscopic vision given them by the large median eyes.)

Jumping spiders are active, diurnal hunters, moving around with quick darts and long leaps. Before each leap, the spider lays down an attachment disc to the substrate, and then an anchor line to this so that if the object aimed for is missed or the spider doesn't land on solid ground, it can haul itself back to safety. The smaller eyes around the large anterior median eyes perceive movement and this is why once the prey has been located the spider will rapidly turn and align itself with the target, looking directly at it. The movable retinas of the main eyes compensate for the spider's overall narrow vision, and it is the reflection of this movement that gives the eyes their 'gaze-like' quality. (The fact that jumping spiders can see well can be demonstrated by setting up a mirror in front of a male — the mirror image is threatened as if it were a real conspecific opponent.)

Dandy, displaying

Some species of salticids mimic ants, with which they live. Holding their first pair of legs aloft to mimic feelers, they take on the coloration and 'look' of the ants and may even mimic the ants' typical searching gait. Other spiders also mimic ants, but none as well as the jumping spiders.

They do not spin a web, but do make a sac-like nest, varying from a thickish white sheet to several layers of transparent sheeting. Used as a retreat or as an incubator for the egg sac, these sacs are found on the florescence of grass tufts and rolled-up leaves, in cavities under rocks and old tin cans, and sometimes even in the empty shells of dried-out beetles! One very interesting hide retreat used by salticids are the bulbous and enlarged thorns of some *Acacia* species. If you can find the small hole or holes at the confluence of these thorns and split them open, you will probably find the web retreat, and in many cases the spider as well.

FAMILY: Scytodidae

SPITTING SPIDERS

COMMON GENUS: *Scytodes*

 ·   ·

LIFESTYLE: Free-running, ground-living
HABITAT: In built-up areas; on rocks or in crevices of rocks; in and under leaf litter and rotting logs
SIZE: Small to medium-large. 3,5–15 mm (leg span up to 33 mm). Female larger than male
NOCTURNAL
POISON: Harmless
COLLECTING METHODS: Hand-to-jar; pitfall trap; pooter; rock turning

Scytodes is easily recognized by the shape of its carapace, which is lofty and rounded in the thoracic region, sloping downwards towards the anterior aspect. It has six eyes arranged in three well-separated pairs. It varies in colour from pale yellow to dark brown, with a series of dark, symmetrical patterns on its dorsal aspect. The legs are long and delicate (see plate 36).

Some species are found in and around human habitations, especially near rubble and dustbins. They move slowly in dark cor-

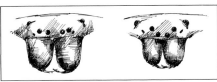

Eye patterns

ners, stalking their prey, and have been found often in closets and dark cupboards.

Spitting spiders are hunters, wandering in search of prey. When this is located, it is immobilized by the fine strings of a poisonous, sticky secretion ejected by the spider. By rapidly vibrating the chelicerae from side to side, *Scytodes* is able to zigzag the sticky strings across and over the prey, as a net, transfixing it to the substrate.

The egg sac is carried in the chelicerae, rather in the same manner as the pholcids (see page 69). Preying on fishmoths and other soft-bodied pests, these are definitely spiders to be encouraged in the home.

Spitting spider, with prey

FAMILY: **Selenopidae**

WALL CRAB SPIDERS OR 'FLATTIES'

COMMON GENERA: *Anyphops, Selenops*

 ·   ·

LIFESTYLE: Free-running, ground-living
HABITAT: In built-up areas; on or under bark; on rocks or in crevices of rocks
SIZE: Large to very large. 15–>30 mm
DIURNAL / NOCTURNAL
POISON: Harmless
COLLECTING METHODS: Hand-to-jar; rock turning

The wall crab spiders are common in houses, especially in the eastern regions of southern Africa. They have an extremely flattened body, with legs that spread out in a crab-like fashion. This makes them most distinctive and recognizable as they sit, usually face down, on the wall. They are distinguished from the large wandering crab spiders (see page 97) by having six eyes forming a front row, with two larger eyes posteriorly forming the second row. In *Anyphops* the anterior row of eyes is recurved. In *Selenops* the anterior row is rather straight. 'Flatties' are large, mottled brown to black, and are extremely agile and fast-running if disturbed. Long spines are present at intervals on the thin legs.

'Flatties' are possibly most often seen indoors because their cryptic coloration makes them almost invisible on trees and rocks. Furthermore, their frozen stance makes for perfect camouflage when resting on anything but a plain-coloured wall (see plate 34). When moving undisturbed their gait is likened to that of the large rain spiders, the heteropodids (see page 97). Because of their flattened body they can disappear behind skirting boards, behind hanging pictures and into seemingly inaccessible places.

Eggs are laid in a disc-shaped, papery, smooth, white cocoon, secured against the substrate. These discs, 5 cm in diameter, are seen against the sides of wooden beams and gumpoles supporting thatched roofs, in garden sheds and outbuildings.

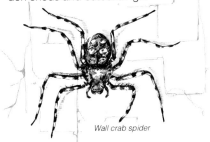

Wall crab spider

FAMILY: Sicariidae
SIX-EYED CRAB SPIDERS
COMMON GENUS: *Sicarius*

 •   •

LIFESTYLE: Free-running, ground-living
HABITAT: On or under sand; in semi-arid desert
SIZE: Medium to medium-large. 8–15 mm (leg span up to 30 mm)
DIURNAL / NOCTURNAL
POISON: Venomous. Six-eyed crab spiders are known to have a virulent cytotoxic poison, but its effects are not well documented in man. Recorded bites have caused severe ulcerative wounds with tissue damage at all levels, and death in one case. It appears that the poison destroys not only the tissue structure in the vicinity of the bite but tissue throughout the body, causing massive internal haemorrhaging and necrosis.
COLLECTING METHODS: Hand-to-jar

Six-eyed crab spider

Sicarius is a six-eyed spider with a flattened body, thickish legs for its size, and a coriaceous integument which is usually covered with sand particles. The legs are extended sideways and held close to the substrate (see plate 57). The eyes are in three pairs and set on the front of the flattened carapace, which tends to make the spider look squint.

Sicarius lives on and in the sand in the semi-arid regions of southern Africa. Its brownish body, often covered with sand particles, blends in well with the environment, and when stationary it is almost impossible to see. A sudden dash and dive into the sand is what invariably gives it away; it is amazing how quickly it can disappear by throwing sand over its body with its legs.

These spiders make no web of any kind and are hunters, relying on ambush to overcome their prey. Provided with a stridulatory organ, they are said to produce a faint humming sound. In captivity they have been known to live for several years.

Grass Spiders

FAMILY: Philodromidae
SMALL WANDERING CRAB-SPIDERS
COMMON GENERA: *Philodromus, Thanatus, Hirriusa, Ebo, Tibellus, Suemus*

 •

LIFESTYLE: Free-running, plant-living
HABITAT: In and up trees; on rocks or in crevices of rocks; on bushes and plants or in low base vegetation; in, on or under grass; in and under leaf litter and rotting logs
SIZE: Small to medium-large. 4–12 mm
DIURNAL / NOCTURNAL
POISON: Harmless
COLLECTING METHODS: Sweep-netting; beating; hand-to-jar; tree trap

The philodromid spiders have a slightly flattened body with slender, laterigrade legs that are mostly of equal length and thickness. Claw tufts are present. There are teeth on the promargin of the chelicerae, unlike those of the thomisids (see page 109). The eyes are almost the same size and are positioned in two recurved rows. Most species have an elongate to oval abdomen, flattened dorsoventrally and often having chevron markings. The mottled yellow and brown body blends with the habitat surroundings. *Ebo* has the second pair of legs much longer than the rest.

Philodromus sp.

Most species are tree- or grass-living and are wanderers. As with other wanderers, they are swift and aggressive in pursuing prey. *Philodromus* is found on trunks of trees and on bushes. *Tibellus* is more often collected while grass-sweeping. *Hirriusa*, *Thanatus* and *Suemus* are mainly cursorial. *Ebo* is most often found after beating *Acacia* trees.

This family was previously regarded as a subfamily of Thomisidae. There is a resemblance in the way they hold out their legs, hence the inclusion of the word 'crab' in the common name. Although much smaller, they also bear a resemblance to the families Heteropodidae (see page 97) and Selenopidae (see page 107).

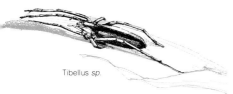

Tibellus sp.

Flower Spiders

FAMILY: Thomisidae

SMALL CRAB SPIDERS

The family Thomisidae consists of four subfamilies: Misumeninae, Bominae, Stiphropodinae and Stephanopinae. We will consider only the first two subfamilies, as the second two are currently being revised and, being uncommon, are less likely to be encountered by the amateur.

LIFESTYLE: Sedentary, ground-living; sedentary, plant-living
HABITAT: In and up trees; on or under bark; in webbing, scrapes or free-running, under stones; on rocks or in crevices of rocks; on bushes and plants or in low base vegetation; in, on or under grass; on flowers and leaves
SIZE: Medium to medium-large. 8–15 mm
DIURNAL / NOCTURNAL
POISON: Harmless
COLLECTING METHODS: Sweep-netting; beating; hand-to-jar; rock turning

SUBFAMILY: **Misumeninae**

COMMON GENERA: *Thomisus*, *Runcinia*, *Synaema*, *Diaea*, *Tmarus*, *Monaeses*, *Misumenops*, *Pherecydes*, *Xysticus*

SUBFAMILY: **Bominae**

COMMON GENERA: *Holopelus*, *Avelis*, *Parabomis*

Small crab spiders are well known and have been researched in detail in South Africa by Dr Ansie Dippenaar of the Plant Protection Research Institute. The superficial resemblance of some species to crabs, as well as their ability to move sideways and backwards with ease, has given them their common name.

Small crab-spider

109

Most species have a short, wide and slightly flattened body, with the legs directed sideways and with the two front pairs usually longer and more powerful than the rest. The eye pattern, which although in itself varies between the genera, is distinctive to the family and highly diagnostic. The lateral eyes are either separate or on conjoined tubercles. In many genera of the subfamily Misumeninae the eyes are situated on distinct tubercles (as in *Thomisus),* on a carina (as in *Runcinia)* or on a protuberance (as in *Pherecydes).* In others, the eyes are on small swellings.

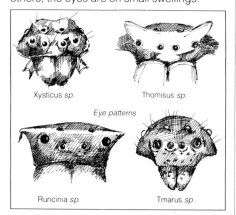

Xysticus *sp.* Thomisus *sp.*

Eye patterns

Runcinia *sp.* Tmarus *sp.*

The Misumeninae are usually found on plants. In general, they are sluggish spiders. *Thomisus* is common on flowers. They have the ability to slowly change colour depending on the shade of the flower, and vary in colour from white to yellow to pink (see plates 38 and 39). *Misumenops,* coloured in bright greens and reds, is also found on flowers.

Thomisids found on grass usually have a long, narrow body. Their colour is that of the grass on which they are found, with dark longitudinal lines resembling the veins of the grass blades, as in *Monaeses* and *Runcinia* (see plate 42). Genera found on seeds are hairy, with a spiky appearance.

Tmarus is found on the bark of trees and *Pherecydes* in the bark crevices. *Xysticus,* a drab, dark brown spider, is found on and under stones and sometimes on tree bark.

Members of the subfamily Bominae are small spiders, characterized by a globular-shaped body, a thick, granulous integument and short legs. They live on plants, mainly grass and flowering herbs.

Small crab spiders are expert ambushers and do not spin webs. They live mainly on plants, patiently awaiting prey to alight near them. They appear sluggish and lethargic — only to be transformed into a flash of movement as they pounce on and over prey that strays too near. They rely on touch rather than sight to capture their prey, and on their stillness and coloration to protect them from predators. They are formidable spiders and will attack insects and other spiders much larger than themselves. They have a potent venom which can kill a bee within seconds. Holding the prey in their chelicerae, they literally suck it dry, discarding the empty shell of the insect.

Foliage Spiders

FAMILY: Oxyopidae

LYNX SPIDERS

COMMON GENERA: *Oxyopes* (golden lynx spiders), *Peucetia* (green lynx spiders), *Hamataliwa* (dome head lynx spiders incorporates those species previously listed under *Oxyopedon,*)

 ·   ·

LIFESTYLE: Free-running, plant-living
HABITAT: On bushes and plants or in low base vegetation; in, on or under grass; on flowers or leaves
SIZE: Small to medium-large. 4–16 mm (some larger species of *Peucetia* may have a leg span of up to 40 mm)
DIURNAL
POISON: Harmless
COLLECTING METHODS: Sweep-netting; beating; hand-to-jar

Lynx spider

Lynx spiders may be immediately recognized by the numerous spines standing out at right angles on their legs, and in some species by their bright colours. They have a high and angular carapace that is flattened in front, with a wide clypeus and a distinctive eye pattern. The abdomen in all species tapers to a point behind (see plate 40).

Oxyopes and *Hamataliwa* are smaller in size than *Peucetia*, which can display a variety of colours, from bright green to yellow and red-black markings. *Oxyopes*, which is very common on plants, also varies in colour, from bright yellow-green to dull brown. *Hamataliwa* is a rather drab brown colour, but is easily recognized as a member of the family by its typical spines, and as a member of the genus by the presence of little tufts of hair growing out above the eyes. The carapace is obviously dome-shaped.

These spiders live on plants. Their common name is indicative of their cat-like behaviour of stalking and jumping at prey. They can be seen leaping with great ease through the leaves of low shrubs and bushes, either chasing prey or escaping from predators. Some species can jump more than 2 cm into the air to seize a passing insect in full flight.

Some species of *Peucetia* are more sedentary, favouring glandular (succulent) plants. Insects seem to become trapped on these plants, thus providing instant food for the lynx spider inhabitant.

No web is made by this family; the silk is used as a safety drag line when the spider is jumping, and for anchoring the egg sac to vegetation. The egg sacs are fastened to a twig or suspended among silken threads laid between twigs and leaves, and are guarded by the female. She stays with the eggs, not eating, until they hatch and she dies.

Bark Spiders

FAMILY: **Hersiliidae**
LONG-SPINNERED SPIDERS
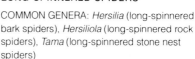

COMMON GENERA: *Hersilia* (long-spinnered bark spiders), *Hersiliola* (long-spinnered rock spiders), *Tama* (long-spinnered stone nest spiders)

  ·   ·

LIFESTYLE: Free-running, ground-living; free-running, plant living
HABITAT: On or under bark; in webbing, scrapes or free-running, under stones; on rocks or in crevices of rocks
SIZE: Medium-large to large. 10–20 mm
DIURNAL
POISON: Harmless
COLLECTING METHODS: Hand-to-jar; rock turning

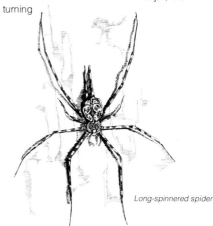

Long-spinnered spider

Hersiliids are flat spiders with two long spinnerets protruding way past the posterior end of the abdomen. They are usually seen resting upside-down with legs outstretched on the bark of trees or the sides of rocks. The eyes are generally in two strongly recurved rows, situated on a large protuberance at the front of the carapace. Their colour is variable, from grey to brown and even a speckled black, and it has been reported that they may undergo a certain amount of colour change depending on the background on which they are resting. The carapace and abdomen are flattened and the abdomen is most often wider behind than it is in front. The legs are fairly robust and are held out in a star-like fashion; they have the same cryptic coloration as the spider.

Hersilia is found on the bark of trees and is difficult to see. The flattened body reduces shadows and the speckled coloration blends in with the background (see plate 41). This camouflage is destroyed only by movement, when the spider is disturbed. It is reported that should you mark the eight points at which the legs rest, then disturb the spider so it moves away, it will return after a time and take up the identical position.

Hersiliola and *Tama* are found on and among rocks. Their behaviour is very similar to that of *Hersilia*, but *Tama* is said to spin an irregular web rather like that of the pholcid spiders (see page 69). They also make a nest of loose webbing encompassing small stones and leaf debris. This retreat may appear as a spreading network of fine threads extending outwards for up to 23 cm.

Hersiliids enswathe their prey, emitting silk from the long spinnerets while these are rotated rapidly across and around the victim.

FAMILY: **Trochanteriidae**

SCORPION SPIDERS

COMMON GENUS: *Platyoides*

LIFESTYLE: Free-running, ground-living; free-running, plant-living
HABITAT: In built-up areas; on or under bark; in scrapes or free-running, under stones; in and under leaf litter and rotting logs
SIZE: Medium-large to large. 12–30 mm
DIURNAL / NOCTURNAL
POISON: Harmless
COLLECTING METHODS: Beating; hand-to-jar; pitfall trap; tree trap

Scorpion spider

These are extremely flattened spiders. Their scorpion-like legs are held sideways, with some of them doubling back over the body, giving the spider a most unspider-like look (see plate 43).

They are mostly dark brown or grey, with the flat carapace and abdomen darker than the legs. In some, the abdomen shows white patterns. In front of the flattened carapace are enlarged, projecting chelicerae with long fangs. At rest the femur, patella and tibia of the second, third and fourth legs are folded in, over and across the abdomen respectively. This positioning of the legs is facilitated by the fact that the trochanters of the legs, especially the fourth leg, are very elongated.

Wandering spiders, they do not build webs. With their flattened body, they are found mainly under bark and stones, in leaf litter and often in and about human habitations under flower pots.

Scorpion spiders are common throughout southern Africa, but only in four of the 10 species described thus far is anything about the males known.

MYGALOMORPHS

Mygalomorphs belong to the suborder Orthognatha, which is thought to be a primitive group. They are characterized by having two pairs of booklungs and paraxial chelicerae that strike forwards and downwards. Most mygalomorphs are medium to large spiders and many of them are sedentary ground-dwellers.

FAMILY: *Atypidae*
PURSE-WEB SPIDERS

COMMON GENUS: *Calommata* (African purse-web spiders)

LIFESTYLE: Sedentary, ground-living
HABITAT: Silken tube
SIZE: Large. 15–30 mm
DIURNAL / NOCTURNAL
POISON: Harmless
COLLECTING METHOD: Hand-to-jar

Purse-web spider

The atypids are a small group of mygalomorph spiders which live permanently in a silken tube. Their chelicerae, which are used to impale their prey through the tube, are large and dorsally expanded with long fangs and enormously elongated endites. Their eyes are situated on a small ocular protuberance near the edge of the clypeus. The size of their legs, especially the femur, is greatly reduced. A single species, *C. simoni*, has been described from southern Africa.

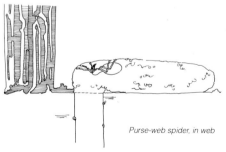

Purse-web spider, in web

The spider impales a moth through the web

This smallish mygalomorph spider spends its entire life within a silken tube sealed at both ends and camouflaged with bits of debris. Half the tube protrudes above the ground, either supported up the side of a bank or tree trunk, or forming a 90-degree angle where it leaves the substrate and runs for about 30 cm along the ground. The section above the ground resembles a narrow purse, hence the common name. The spider attacks any insect that lands on the tube by biting through it and impaling the victim with its long fangs. After injecting the poison and immobilizing its prey, the spider pulls it through a hole cut by the chelicerae for this purpose, consumes it and ejects the remains through the same hole. The spider then sets about repairing the damaged tube and awaits its next victim.

Calommata may be very aggressive if taken from its tube-web home.

FAMILY: *Barychelidae*
LESSER BABOON SPIDERS

COMMON GENERA: *Pisenor, Sipalolasma*

LIFESTYLE: Sedentary, ground-living
HABITAT: In webbing or scrapes, under stones; in burrows
SIZE: Medium-large to large. 12–30 mm
DIURNAL / NOCTURNAL

POISON: Harmless
COLLECTING METHODS: Hand-to-jar; pitfall trap; digging; rock turning

Much smaller than their cousins the Theraphosidae (see page 120), lesser baboon spiders also differ from the Theraphosidae in having the apical segment of the posterior lateral spinnerets shorter than the rest, and in having the anterior lobe of the maxillae only weakly developed, if at all. The barychelids have only two claws, with the scopulae on the tarsi of the first and second legs well developed and iridescent. The carapace and legs are uniformly setose. The carapace is as high in front of the fovea as it is behind.

In *Pisenor* the clypeus is absent and the eyes on the anterior margin are widely spaced. In *Sipalolasma* a clypeus is present and the eight eyes are situated in a rectangular group slightly further back on the carapace. The thoracic fovea is a deep, circular pit. A tibial spur is present in the males.

Most species build a silk-lined burrow in the ground. The burrow often has a 'Y' formation, either with both entrances open or with one ending blind just below the surface. When digging up the burrow, you may find the spider hiding in the blind-ending tunnel.

Lesser baboon spiders are aggressive and can move swiftly if threatened.

Lesser baboon spider

FAMILY: Ctenizidae

TRAPDOOR SPIDERS

COMMON GENUS: *Stasimopus*

 · ·

LIFESTYLE: Sedentary, ground-living
HABITAT: In burrows
SIZE: Medium-large to very large. 10–36 mm
NOCTURNAL
POISON: Harmless
COLLECTING METHODS: Hand-to-jar; digging; pitfall trap

Trapdoor spider, at entrance to burrow

The Ctenizidae are large spiders, characterized by the female having bands of short, stout, thorn-like spines on the lateral surface of the anterior legs. Most of the species have a short, thick-set body lacking the hairy appearance of the family Theraphosidae (see page 120). They are equipped with a rastellum, a spiny rake on the outer portion of the jaws, which they use to dig tubular burrows. The shortish legs are covered with spines and are usually very robust (see plate 44).

All species dig burrows, which vary in shape and design but all of which are protected by a hinged, tight-fitting, reinforced lid which is almost invisible when closed (see plate 45). When threatened by predators, the spider uses the spines on its short, robust legs to grip the burrow wall and under-surface of the trapdoor. It displays amazing strength in holding the trapdoor shut.

Not much has been written about the behaviour of trapdoor spiders because their secluded lifestyle makes them difficult to study.

This family is widely distributed throughout southern Africa.

FAMILY: Cyrtaucheniidae
LESSER TRAPDOOR SPIDERS

 ·   ·

Carapace of
Homostola sp.

LIFESTYLE: Sedentary, ground-living
HABITAT: In burrows; in semi-arid desert
SIZE: Medium to medium-large. 8–15 mm
NOCTURNAL
POISON: Harmless
COLLECTING METHODS: Hand-to-jar; digging

SUBFAMILY: Cyrtaucheniinae

COMMON GENUS: *Homostola*

SUBFAMILY: Aporoptychinae

COMMON GENUS: *Ancylotrypa*

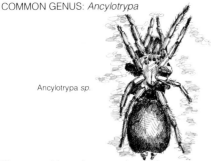

Ancylotrypa *sp.*

These spiders have gained the common name lesser trapdoor spiders because a rastellum is present in both South African genera. *Homostola*, known only from female specimens, has a lightly hirsute carapace with a strongly arched caput. The fovea is broad and procurved, and the eyes are set on a distinctly raised tubercle which is twice as wide as it is long and is positioned anteriorly. There is thus no clypeus. A rastellum consisting of several spines is present on the inner distal surface of the broad chelicerae.

The carapace of *Ancyloptrypa* is glabrous and is broader anteriorly than posteriorly. As in *Homostola*, the fovea is broad and procurved and the clypeus is absent. However, the rectangular eye group is positioned on a weakly developed tubercle. The chelicerae are prorect and a rastellum, similar to that in *Homostola*, is present.

Behaviour patterns for these shy ground-dwellers are not well documented, partly because they live in burrows, but also because the family has not been studied in any detail. Cyrtauchenids collected by the author have all been found in semi-open or closed burrows in soft or sandy soil. In Namibia, burrows with lids of loosely bound sand particles in a mass of webbing were surrounded by lumps of sand and webbing. These burrows, on the ridges of sand dunes, often went down over 60 cm, and dealing with the collapsing sand made it difficult to capture every specimen.

It is assumed that the method of prey capture is similar to that used by the other trapdoor spiders (see pages 115, 117 and 119).

FAMILY: Dipluridae
FUNNEL-WEB MYGALOMORPHS

COMMON GENERA: *Allothele*, *Thelechoris* (incorporates southern African species previously listed under *Ischnothele*)

 ·

LIFESTYLE: Sedentary, plant-living
HABITAT: In and up trees; on or under bark; on rocks or in crevices of rocks; in and under leaf litter and rotting logs
SIZE: Medium to medium-large. 8–15 mm
DIURNAL / NOCTURNAL
POISON: Harmless
COLLECTING METHOD: Hand-to-jar

In comparison with some of the other large terrestrial mygalomorphs, the funnel-web species are smaller, more slender and immediately recognizable by their long, widely separated posterior spinnerets (which are sometimes half the length of the abdomen or more). The carapace is very low and hirsute

Spinnerets

and the fovea small and pit-like. The eyes are on a raised tubercle which is about twice as long as it is wide. The chelicerae are porrect and lack a rastellum. Diplurids have three claws with spinose tarsi. These are, however, totally lacking scopulae, a feature which distinguishes them from the family Nemesiidae (see page 119).

These mygalomorphs are mostly arboreal. If flushed from their hiding place in the corner of their web they can be most aggressive. Although smaller, they are unmistakably relatives of the trapdoor and baboon spiders (see pages 115 and 120). They are widespread throughout southern Africa.

The funnel-web mygalomorphs build a rather large, nondescript sheet web, a messy webbing of bluish tinge and cloth-like texture. The web is found in the forks of trees, in crevices of fallen trees and stumps, among the roots at the base of trees and, sometimes, in the crevices of large rock formations. Roughly tubular in shape, it has exits at both ends and a heavier midsection or retreat.

Funnel-web mygalomorph

FAMILY: **Idiopidae**

FRONT-EYED TRAPDOOR SPIDERS

COMMON GENERA: *Ctenolophus, Gorgyrella, Galeosoma, Heligmomerus, Idiops, Segregara*

 · ·

LIFESTYLE: Sedentary, ground-living
HABITAT: In burrows
SIZE: Medium-large to large. 12–20 mm
NOCTURNAL
POISON: Harmless
COLLECTING METHODS: Hand-to-jar; digging

The genera of this family are the four-lunged trapdoor spiders that were previously placed under the family Ctenizidae (see page 115). These genera have three unique taxonomic characteristics that distinguish them from the Ctenizidae (Raven, 1985), which are of importance to the professional arachnologist. Within the family there are three subfamilies, of which only Idiopinae is known to occur in the region.

SUBFAMILY: **Idiopinae**

These trapdoor spiders have the anterior lateral eyes close together at the edge of the clypeus, well forward of the other eyes, which are set on a tubercle (see plate 46). They all

Galeosoma sp.

117

possess a rastellum, and have a glabrous carapace with a strongly procurved fovea. The tarsi and metatarsi of the first leg have numerous lateral spines, and all tarsi of the male show scopulae. Scopulae are absent in the females.

As with other trapdoor spiders, the rastellum is used to dig the burrow in which it lives. The burrow is closed with a 'trapdoor' which varies from a thin, wafer-like flap to a thickish, cork-like door. Burrow-bound during the day, the spider usually sits at the mouth of the burrow, door ajar, with its legs slightly protruding, waiting for prey to pass by. Once disturbed or in possession of prey, the spider retreats into the burrow, closing the door tightly behind it.

In defence the spider is able to hold down the trapdoor with great force; it is difficult to prise open, even with a sturdy knife.

Trapdoor spiders occur close to one another in rather specific habitats, so that when one hole is spotted you can be fairly sure that there will be other burrows nearby.

Galeosoma females and juveniles are unique in having the posterior dorsal aspect of the abdomen truncated and chitinized. This 'shield' is used by the spider to block the burrow and its lower chambers in case of attack. While retreating she presents the shield to the invader. The door of the *Galeosoma* burrow is of the wafer-like type.

Idiops's door is the cork-like type, and is so tight-fitting and well camouflaged that it takes an expert to find it. Most often the colony site is found when one spider's death results in its trapdoor being left hanging loosely open.

FAMILY: **Microstigmatidae**

DWARF MYGALOMORPHS

COMMON GENUS: *Microstigmata*

LIFESTYLE: Free-running, ground-living
HABITAT: In webbing or scrapes, under stones; in and under leaf litter and rotting logs; in forests
SIZE: Small to medium-large. 4,5-12,5 mm
DIURNAL / NOCTURNAL
POISON: Harmless
COLLECTING METHODS: Hand-to-jar; pitfall trap; tullgren funnel; sifting

Dwarf mygalomorph

Found living in the forest humus especially along the coastal forests of Natal, this mygalomorph seems restricted to habitats offering high humidity and even temperatures. Its body is glabrous but has weak, blunt-tipped or clavate setae. The back legs project far behind the abdomen. It is characterized by its habit of encrusting its body with bits of dirt.

It does not appear to make a burrow or a retreat of any kind, and seems to make only

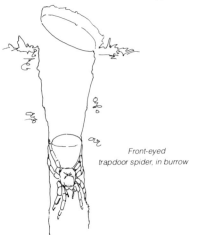

Front-eyed trapdoor spider, in burrow

minimal use of silk. It appears that the spider lives under stones and fallen logs on the forest floor. In captivity, *Microstigmata* is somewhat aggressive and feeds predominantly on small insects.

FAMILY: Migidae

BANDED-LEGGED AND TREE TRAPDOOR SPIDERS

COMMON GENERA: *Moggridgea*, *Poecilomigas*

 ·   ·

LIFESTYLE: Sedentary, plant-living or on rocks
HABITAT: In and up trees; on or under bark; on rocks or in crevices of rocks
SIZE: Medium to large. 8–25 mm
NOCTURNAL
POISON: Harmless
COLLECTING METHOD: Hand-to-jar

Arboreal mygalomorphs similar in appearance to the Ctenizidae (see page 115), the Migidae live in tunnels with trapdoors, situated on trees or on rock faces.

Since they do not dig their tunnel, they have no rastellum on the chelicerae. The eyes are arranged in two wide rows and are not situated on a tubercle. The spiders appear to be quite squat, with short, thick legs tapering towards the tarsi, and are mostly dark brown to black in colour. *Poecilomigas* has clearly banded legs, making it a most distinctive, easily recognized spider.

Banded-legged trapdoor spider

A tough tunnel web is made as a retreat, on the bark of a tree or on a rock face, with a trapdoor at each end (in the case of *Poecilomigas*) or with only an upper trapdoor (in *Moggridgea*); if *Poecilomigas* has used a crevice in a tree or rock as its retreat, then only one trapdoor lid will be visible to the outside world. It is very difficult to find these 'flattened' trapdoor tubes as they are covered with pieces of lichen and moss and, very often, with pieces of the bark of the tree on which they are made.

Although small, migid spiders can be most aggressive when flushed from their retreats.

FAMILY: Nemesiidae

SHORT-SPINNERED FUNNEL-WEB MYGALOMORPHS

COMMON GENERA: *Hermacha* (incorporates those species previously listed under *Hermachola*), *Spiroctenus*, *Pionothele*, *Entypesa*, *Lepthercus*

 ·   ·

LIFESTYLE: Sedentary, ground-living
HABITAT: In webbing, under stones; in and under leaf litter
SIZE: Medium to medium-large. 8–15 mm
NOCTURNAL
POISON: Harmless
COLLECTING METHOD: Hand-to-jar

These spiders are distinguished from the family Dipluridae (see page 116) in having the posterior lateral spinnerets much shorter and closer together. The carapace is low and hirsute. The eight eyes are situated in two rows on a low tubercle. The fovea is short and straight. The chelicerae are porrect and broad, and lack a rastellum. Nemesiids have three claws like their cousins the diplurids, and in addition have well-developed scopulae on the tarsi.

Very little is known about their specific behaviour, but I have collected these spiders

119

mainly from tubular retreats under rocks. The tube of these has never gone deeper than about 12 cm below the surface. Often there is more than one branch to the tube. The webbing does not have the characteristic blue tinge of the diplurid spiders.

Three subfamilies are known to occur in southern Africa.

FAMILY: Theraphosidae
TARANTULAS OR BABOON SPIDERS

COMMON GENERA: *Harpactira* (common baboon spiders), *Ceratogyrus*, (horned baboon spiders), *Pterinochilus* (golden-brown baboon spiders), *Harpactirella* (small baboon spiders), *Coelogenium* (Zimbabwe golden-yellow baboon spiders), *Brachionopus*

LIFESTYLE: Sedentary, ground-living
HABITAT: In burrows
SIZE: Very large. >35 mm
NOCTURNAL
POISON: Some venomous, others harmless. Owing to their size, especially the size of the chelicerae, baboon spiders can inflict a painful wound. The poison of the larger members is only mildly toxic to man; that of the small baboon spider, *Harpactirella lightfooti*, from the south-western Cape, is said to be neurotoxic and possibly dangerous to man. This should be heeded if you are accidentally bitten, and should the bite symptoms become severe it is suggested that the antivenom used for the black button spider's bite be administered. The antivenom is available from the Medical Research Institute in Johannesburg.
COLLECTING METHODS: Hand-to-jar; night collecting; pitfall trap; digging

Pterinochilus sp.

The spider originally referred to as a tarantula was the European wolf spider, *Lycosa tarantula*, which was large and hairy and found living in burrows. Later, as people moved into new territories, any large, hairy spider, and especially those of the family Theraphosidae, was labelled a tarantula. In southern Africa they also became known as baboon spiders, not only for their hairy appearance but also for the fact that the pads of the spiders' tarsi resemble the colour and texture of the pad of a monkey's or baboon's foot.

Baboon spiders are very large and hairy, with heavy legs that retain the basal diameter throughout the length of the leg. They have large, hairy pedipalps which look rather like another pair of legs. They are distinguished from the barychelids (see page 114) by the presence of a distinct lobe on the anterior aspect of the maxillae.

The theraphosids in the region belong to the subfamily Harpacterinae and are characterized by having a patch of erect to semi-erect, feathery setae on the retrolateral surface of the chelicerae (some authors refer to this as a 'plumose pad'). A second characteristic of great taxonomic importance is the wide clypeus present in all genera.

The eight small eyes are arranged on an occular protuberance on the front portion of the carapace, behind the clypeus.

Ceratogyrus is distinguished from *Harpactira* and *Pterinochilus* by having a large horn in the centre of its carapace, sloping either forwards or backwards according to the species (see plate 47). This genus presents in a range of dull colours, from silver-grey to black. The joints of the legs show typical narrow white bands.

Pterinochilus may vary in colour from grey-yellow to bright orange; indeed, *Petrinochilus* has the common name golden-brown baboon spider (see plate 48). *Harpactira* is usually darker brown in colour and slightly smaller than the previous two genera (see plate 49). Both *Pterinochilus* and *Harpactira* have the plumose pad on the upper, outer surface of the chelicerae. The two genera may be told apart by the row of stiff setae underneath the patch that are present only in *Harpactira*.

Harpactirella *sp.*

Coelogenium is about the same size as *Harpactira* but is brownish-yellow in colour. It is unique in this family in having the fovea procurved in a complete 'U' shape.

Both *Brachionopus* and *Harpactirella* (see plate 50) are smaller and more slender and graceful than the previous genera. They lack the chelicereal scopula, but because of the presence of other taxonomic characteristics are included in this subfamily. The spinnerets are very long and protrude beyond the posterior end of the abdomen.

Theraphosid spiders are found throughout southern Africa, generally in the warmer, more arid areas. They live underground, in open-ended, silk-lined burrows, emerging only at night to hunt and never moving very far from

Ceratogyrus *sp.*

the burrow. (Males may, however, be found wandering freely in search of a mate.)

Normally slow-moving, baboon spiders can be taunted into aggressive action, whereupon they will rear up, forelegs in the air, exposing the blood-red hairs on the chelicerae and black underparts (see plate 51).

Recent observations have suggested that the burrow entrances of the different genera vary. It has been found, for example, that those of *Ceratogyrus* are flush with the surrounding substrate while those of *Pterinochilus* are raised some 2 cm above the substrate, with grass, leaves or twigs woven into the extended silk lining.

Much in demand as pets, baboon spiders have been recorded as living as long as 20 years. Once removed from a mature burrow they are unable to dig a new one as they do not have a rastellum on the chelicerae as do the ctenizids. Forced to live in captivity, they construct a sheet-like mass of web on the substrate, attached to high points, giving a hammock-like appearance. They may then take up a position in the corner of the sheet or below one of the raised points.

Baboon spider, in threatening pose

GLOSSARY

Arboreal Living in or among trees (see Terrestrial)

Anal tubercle Tubercle at the end of the abdomen, bearing the anus

Anthropomorphism The attribution of human form or behaviour to an animal

Arachnid A class of arthropods characterized by having simple eyes and four pairs of legs

Araneomorph spiders So-called 'true spiders', having diaxial fangs

Arthropoda An assemblage of phyla, all of which possess an exoskeleton and jointed limbs

Booklung A chamber connected with the atmosphere that the spider uses for breathing.

Calamistrum A row of curved, toothed setae on the metatarsus of the fourth leg of cribellate spiders, used to comb out silk from the cribellum

Caput The 'head' section of the carapace

Carapace The hard shield covering the top of the cephalothorax

Caudal Concerning the tail

Cephalothorax The fused head and thorax of a spider

Chelicerae The first pair of appendages on the cephalothorax, used for biting, chewing and grasping. The fangs form the piercing part of these appendages

Chevron A pattern consisting of one or more 'V'-shaped stripes, seen on the dorsal aspect of the abdomen of certain spiders

Chitinized Covered with a nitrogen-containing polysaccharide, forming a material of great strength

Clavate setae Club-shaped bristles

Clypeus The area between the front row of eyes and the edge of the carapace

Colulus A small protuberance, usually conical, representing the remnant of the cribellum

Conspecific Belonging to the same species

Contiguous Touching along the side or boundary; in contact

Cribellate Having a cribellum (see Ecribellate)

Cribellum A flattened, sieve-like spinning plate, situated in front of the spinnerets of certain spiders

Cryotozoic Inhabiting crevices

Cryptic fauna The life (in this case the spider life) that lives in forests

Cursorial Having limbs adapted for running

Cytotoxic Poisonous to cells

Diaxial The term applied to chelicerae when the fangs oppose each other

Dimorphism Existing in two forms (used here to indicate the great size difference that exists in certain families between the male and female)

Diurnal Active during the day

Dorsal The upper surface

Ecdysis Another name for moulting, during which the old exoskeleton is shed and replaced by a new one

Ecribellate Lacking a cribellum (see Cribellate)

Endite The name given to the modified coxa of the pedipalps, which are used as chewing mouthparts (see Maxillae)

Entelegene The term given to those spiders with complicated reproductive organs

Epigastric furrow The ventral opening, in both sexes, that is situated between and slightly behind the booklungs

Epigynum The sclerotized area around the front of the opening of the female genitalia

Fang The piercing part of the spider jaw, through which runs the poison duct

Fovea A pit or depression near the centre of the carapace. Corresponds to the attachment of muscles to the sucking stomach

Foveal horn Horn-like projection near the centre of the carapace

Genus A group, used in classifying organisms, consisting of a number of similar species (pl. genera)

Geotaxis Taxis in which the stimulus is gravitational force. (Thus, when a spider hangs upside-down under its web, it is said to be in negative geotaxis.)

Globose Globe-like in shape

Haplogene The term given to those spiders with simple reproductive organs

Hydrofuge setae Wax-coated setae which are found on the bodies of those spiders living on and in water

Instar The stage in development between any two moults

Integument Skin; any outer protective layer

Kleptoparasite A spider that searches out the prey or stored food of another spider, usually of a different species, and takes it for her own

Laterigrade All legs pointing to the side, rather than directly forwards or backwards

Maxillae The modified coxa of the pedipalp, used as accessory jaws to break up food (see Endite)

Mimicry Where a spider copies the shape of another animal, or some inanimate object such as a stick

Mygalomorph spiders The more primitive spiders, the jaws of which strike forwards and downwards

Neurotoxic Poisonous to nerves

Nocturnal Active during the night

Ocelli The simple light-receptor eyes of a spider

Ovate Shaped like an egg

Palps (Pedipalps) The second pair of appendages on the cephalothorax. In males they bear the external genitalia

Paraxial The term applied to chelicerae where the fangs are parallel to each other

Pectinate With teeth like a comb

Pedicel The waist, or reduced first segment of the abdomen

Pheromone Chemical substance, the release of which into its surroundings by an animal influences the behaviour of other individuals of the same species

Prorect chelicerae Chelicerae that project forward on the same plane as the carapace

Rastellum A group of teeth on the front of the chelicerae, above the fang, used for digging

Retreat A spider's place of hiding, either within the web or away from it, but connected to it by one or more attachment threads

Sclerotized Having a hardened deposition of sclerotin in the cuticle

Scopula A dense brush of hairs on the foot, which allows the spider to grip onto smooth surfaces

Scutum A sclerotized plate on the abdomen

Setae Bristles and hair-like coverings of invertebrates

Slit organs Sensory organs on the exoskeleton that detect stress

Spigots The terminal endings of the spinnerets; each spinneret may have thousands of spigots

Spinnerets The abdominal appendages through which the silk is extruded

Spiracle The pore through which the spider breathes

Stabilimentum A special band, or bands, of silk placed across the centre of the web

Sternum The plate which forms the underside of the cephalothorax

Stridulation Production of sounds by rubbing together of certain modified structures
Substrate Soil or rock surface over which a spider moves or on which it lives
Terrestrial Living on the land (see Arboreal)
Tracheae Internal tubular respiratory organs
Trichobothria Fine sensory hairs acting as 'touch at a distance' receptors, found on certain leg segments
Tubercle Any small, rounded nodule or elevation
Ventral Lower surface; the underside

LIST OF ARACHNOLOGISTS

Dr A. Dippenaar-Schoeman, Plant Protection Research Institute, Private Bag X134, Pretoria 0001
Dr Martin R. Filmer, P.O. Box 81398, Parkhurst 2120
John and Astri LeRoy, P. O. Box 3369, Witbeeck 1729
The Chairman, Spider Club of Southern Africa, c/o P. O. Box 81398, Parkhurst 2120
The Curator Arachnology, Natal Museum, 237 Loop Street, Pietermaritzburg 3201
The Curator Arachnology, National Museum, P. O. Box 266, Bloemfontein 9300
The Curator Arachnology, State Museum, P. O. Box 1203, Windhoek 9000
The Curator Arachnology, Transvaal Museum, P. O. Box 413, Pretoria 0001

FURTHER READING

Bristowe, W.S. *The World of Spiders.* Collins, London, 1958, revised 1971
Dippenaar, A. and N. *Spiders.* De Jager-HAUM, Pretoria, 1987
Foelix, R.F. *Biology of Spiders.* Harvard University Press, Cambridge, Massachusetts, 1982
Levi, H.W. and L.R. *A Guide to Spiders and their kin.* Golder Press, New York, 1968
Newlands, G. *Spiders.* Struik, Cape Town, 1986, revised 1990
Preston-Mafham, R. and K. *Spiders of the World.* Brandford Press, Poole, Dorset, 1984
Prins, A. and Leroux, V. *South African Spiders and Scorpions.* Anubis Press, Cape Town, 1986
Smith, A. *Baboon Spiders – Tarantulas of Africa and the Middle East.* Fitzgerald Publishing, London, 1990
Yates, J.H. *Spiders of southern Africa.* Books of Africa, Cape Town, 1968

PHOTOGRAPHIC CREDITS

INDEX

INDEX

INDEX

POISONOUS SPIDERS

These spiders are potentially dangerous to man. The symptoms and recommended treatment of a bite are discussed under the main species entry. Also consult 'A Note on Poisons' on page 21.